the Forth Naturalist Historian

Volume 18

Published by the Forth Naturalist and Historian, University of Stirling – an approved charity and member of the Scottish Publishers Association.

ISSN 0309-7560

ISBN 1 898008 07 8

Supported by BP in Scotland.

Cover photograph 'Cattle, 1878' by Joseph Denovan Adam (Smith Art Gallery and Museum, Stirling).

Printed by Meigle Printers Ltd., Tweedbank Industrial Estate, Galashiels.
Set in Zapf Calligraphic on 90gsm Fyneprint and Cream Astralux cover.

THE WEATHER OF 1994

S J Harrison
University of Stirling

History will probably record 1994 as a wet year as floods were an all too familiar feature, particularly in March which, for much of Scotland, was the wettest since records began. Local rivers overtopped their banks no less than four times within the month. The year finished with two wet months and over the weekend of 10th/11th December the Scottish football programme was largely washed out, and there was severe flooding in Glasgow. However, the year was not entirely saturated, May being remarkably dry. As far as temperatures were concerned, spring and summer were generally rather cool and the growing season was late in getting under way. In sharp contrast, November and December were remarkably mild, the former being 3°C warmer than average.

Temperature and rainfall values in the following refer to Parkhead unless otherwise indicated.

January. Unsettled and wet.

Cold Arctic air affected Scotland over the first five days bringing snow to high ground. There was a spell of generally wet and windy weather until the 14th when the clouds cleared. Night temperatures fell below freezing and there were moderate frosts on the 15th, 16th and 17th, the air temperature falling to –4.5°C in Bridge of Allan by the morning of the 16th. There was a dramatic rise in temperature on the 18th and a persistent, and often very strong, westerly wind blew for the next six days. Blustery showers fell as snow, although none accumulated on ground below 500ft (152m). There was a brief respite on the 24th but gales and rain returned on the 25th. The wind veered towards the north on the 27th and temperatures were low in the Arctic air. Snow fell overnight but this lay to a depth of only 10mm in the Forth valley by the morning of the 29th. The wind backed to a milder south-westerly direction after the 29th and temperatures recovered a little by the end of the month.

February. Cold and dull.

Unsettled wet weather continued into February and 24.1mm of rainfall was recorded in Bridge of Allan over the first two days. By the 2nd, the Allan had overtopped its banks. There was a very strong easterly wind in central Scotland on the 3rd. The 9th and 10th were brighter but cloud and rain returned again on the 11th. After the 11th most of the British Isles was affected by a strong and bitterly cold easterly airstream, which persisted until the 18th. There were snow flurries on the 14th, but on the 15th the snow had become heavy and continuous, and the daytime temperature reached only 2.3°C. However, by the evening of the 15th the depth of snow was little more than 20mm on low ground. No further snow fell but, as the clouds cleared, night temperatures fell very sharply and reached –9.5°C by the morning of the 17th (–10.4°C Bridge of Allan). The snow cover froze and lasted until the 18th when the cloud cover returned and improved night temperatures. Daytime temperatures, however, remained low, rising to only 0.6°C on the 20th. A cold continental easterly airstream became re-established from the 20th and snow began to fall again. However, central Scotland escaped the worst of the snow, which affected mainly northern England and southern Scotland. By the 25th, the Met Office was issuing severe weather warnings for Scotland and on the 26th several main roads were impassable in Grampian and Highland Regions. By the end of the month it was the wettest and dullest February since 1923 in parts of eastern and southern Scotland.

March. An exceptionally wet month.

The first two days were relatively calm but from the 2nd there was a protracted period of unsettled and exceptionally wet weather. After 18.2mm of rain had fallen on the 4th (20.8mm Bridge of Allan) the Allan was in flood by the 5th. The weather remained windy and very wet until the 8th by which time the Allan was in flood again for the second time within a week. While the wind remained in the south-west, temperatures remained relatively high and the night temperature only fell to 7.7°C in Bridge of Allan on the 7th/8th. Rain occasionally turned to sleet or snow in blustery showers but the snowline remained above 1000ft (305m) on the Ochil Hills. Rain fell again on the 12th and 13th (27.7mm) and the Allan was again in flood by the 14th. The wind veered westerly then north-westerly from the 15th bringing much colder weather with snow. The snowline on the Ochil Hills dropped to 100ft (31m) on the 16th but had retreated to 1500ft (457m) by the 19th, which was a bright and sunny day. There were moderate overnight air frosts between the 18th and 21st and the grass minimum temperature in Bridge of Allan fell below –5°C. Heavy continuous rain fell from the late afternoon of the 22nd to mid-day on the 23rd, by which time the Allan was in flood for the fourth time in three weeks. The 25th and 26th were sunny and pleasantly warm days, reaching 13.1°C in Bridge of Allan. The interlude was, however, brief as wind and rain returned during the afternoon of the 27th. By the end of the month this had been the wettest March of the century in western Scotland.

April. Cool and unsettled.

Winds were generally fresh west to north-west for the first nine days. The weather was cold and rather unsettled during this period and heavy snow fell on the 4th. Rain on the 8th fell as snow above 500ft (152m). The 12th to 15th were sunny but the 16th and 17th were rather dull with some light drizzle at times. Between the 18th and 21st there were showers which fell as snow over the Grampians. After the following few days were mild with a fresh south westerly breeze and occasional rain. The end of the month was sunny and warm (16.0°C Parkhead, 17.6°C Bridge of Allan).

May. Very dry and sunny.

The first day was sunny and warm but clouds in a mild south-easterly airstream deposited small quantities of orange dust in the Stirling area on the 2nd. The weather then remained unsettled until the 6th. There were heavy showers on the 8th with thunder in the late afternoon. The wind settled in the east from the 10th and temperatures rose in the relatively dry continental air, reaching 20.7°C in Bridge of Allan on the 14th. However, visibility was generally rather poor. The wind backed to north-easterly after the 18th resulting in a moderate ground frost (–3.2°C Bridge of Allan). The dry but fresh north-easterly persisted until the 24th. After this the remainder of the month was bright and sunny, but cool, in polar air. The wind freshened westerly towards the end of the month by which time there had been a continuous spell of 22 rainless days.

June. Mostly cool and cloudy.

A very warm southerly airstream affected the British Isles and on the 1st and 2nd, dust was deposited in light rain. There were spells of very heavy rain accompanied by thunder on the 3rd (19.8mm Bridge of Allan). The wind freshened westerly on the 4th which improved the visibility but occasional light rain fell over the next few days, with lengthy sunny spells. After the 10th there were three warm and sunny days, the air temperature reaching 25.0°C on the 13th. The daytime temperature fell to 17.6°C on the 14th and by the 16th the weather had reverted to an unsettled westerly pattern with mainly west to south-westerly winds and intermittent rain. Warm air from the south raised temperatures from the 27th when the temperature managed to reach 22.3°C but by the end of the month the daytime temperature had exceeded 20.0°C on only five occasions.

July. Warm but cloudy.

The weather was dominated by a warm but rather unsettled south-easterly airstream over the first eight days. The temperature reached 23.0°C on the 8th (24.0°C Bridge of Allan). There was intermittent rain in Scotland until the 15th, which saw the start of a spell of more settled weather. Although the temperature rose, reaching 24.5°C on the 20th (27.1°C Bridge of Allan), the relative humidity remained high, so the air was unpleasantly oppressive at times. There was cloud and rain on the 21st but the warm weather returned on the 22nd and persisted until the end of the month, although there were substantial falls of rain on the 25th (16.2mm) and 31st (9.6mm).

August. Cool and changeable.

Warm and humid weather continued over the first five days, but there were clearer fresher spells from the 6th. The overnight temperature fell to 3.8°C in Bridge of Allan by the morning of the 14th in a light north-westerly breeze. After the 16th the weather became cloudy with spells of light rain, but the skies cleared on the 20th. By the morning of the 24th 31.5mm of rain had fallen (27.0mm Bridge of Allan). The weather remained unsettled for the next three days, with occasional showers, but more protracted spells of heavy rain brought a further 27.9mm on the 27th/28th. Much of this fell in a torrential downpour in the latter part of the morning of the 28th. This rain was very localised, which is indicated by the respective daily totals for Parkhead (21.6mm) and Bridge of Allan (11.2mm) for the 28th.

September. Cool and relatively dry.

The 1st and 2nd were bright sunny days but the 3rd was a dull and wet day (9.1mm). Between the 5th and 11th the weather was cloudy with heavy showers, which were accompanied by thunder on the 7th and 8th. By the 15th there were fresh to strong northerly winds and on the 17th and 18th night temperatures fell to 4.5°C (2.1°C Bridge of Allan). There were three warm sunny days from the 21st, the daytime temperature reaching 18.7°C. Aboyne on Deeside registered a remarkable 23.4°C on the 23rd.

October. Generally cloudy and cool.

Over the first two days there were spells of heavy rain, then temperatures fell quickly on the 3rd in a strengthening northerly airstream. Under clearer skies the minimum temperature fell to –0.7°C by the morning of the 4th (–1.8°C Bridge of Allan), the first of the autumn frosts. The wind then backed to westerly which gusted to force 6 overnight on the 6th/7th. There was early morning fog every day between the 10th and 15th but this often cleared during the morning. The 11th and 12th were particularly warm and sunny (16.0°C). Scotland experienced a cool easterly run of air over the next three days and the daytime temperature reached only 8.8°C on the 17th. Wetter and windier weather dominated the remainder of the month and there was a 72hr rainfall total of 43.4mm (32.9mm Bridge of Allan) between the 20th and 22nd. As the sky cleared briefly a frost was recorded in Bridge of Allan on the morning of the 28th (Air –1.3°C, Ground –2.1°C).

November. Exceptionally warm and very wet at first.

The weather was dull with occasional rain from the 2nd to 4th and the daytime temperature reached an unseasonal 13.8°C in Bridge of Allan. A brief incursion of cold northerly air on the 5th reduced the temperature but by the 6th the warm but wet southerly airstream had returned. Heavy continuous rain began on the 11th and continued almost unabated until the afternoon of the 13th. This was replaced by heavy showers in a south-westerly wind which gusted to gale force overnight 13th/14th. The 4-day rainfall total (11th – 14th) was 54.5mm (45.8mm Bridge of Allan). A fresh showery westerly persisted until late on the 17th bringing yet more rain. A further 24.5mm was recorded on the 17th/18th. Scotland experienced an exceptionally mild south-westerly airstream until the 26th. The daytime temperature rose to 14.4°C on the 23rd having fallen to a remarkable overnight minimum of 12.0°C. The air then became calm and freezing fog formed during the evening of the 29th. The average air temperature over the month was more than 3.0°C higher than the long-term average and in most places it was the warmest November ever recorded.

December. Mostly mild and very wet.

A strong southerly airstream maintained mild but dull weather for two days. There was dense fog on the morning of the 5th but this gave way to rain, which became heavy in a blustery west wind by evening. Overnight rain had turned to snow by the morning of the 8th. The wind backed south-westerly on the 9th and the temperature increased very quickly early on the 10th. However, this was associated with very heavy and continuous rain which persisted until late on the 11th. The weekend's total rainfall amounted to 58.1mm in the Forth Valley but exceeded 115mm in Strathclyde Region. The Allan overtopped its banks, there was severe flooding in the Glasgow area, and the Scottish football programme was almost totally washed out. Temperatures fell very quickly in calm clear air after the 13th and there were moderate to severe frosts on the 14th and 15th. The daytime temperature reached only 3.7°C (1.7°C Bridge of Allan) on the 14th and freezing fog formed in the evening. Rain turned to sleet on low ground by the evening of the 18th. The snowline on the 19th was down to 400ft (122m) on the Ochil Hills. The minimum temperature on the 21st was –5.0°C (–6.0°C Bridge of Allan) after which the daytime temperature struggled to reach only 1.5°C. There was a lengthy spell of unsettled wet weather over the Christmas period. The 25th and 28th were particularly wet days (11.0mm; 13.5mm). However, the 27th was cold with persistent freezing fog all day. The air temperature was relatively low for much of the last ten days of the month in cold unstable Arctic air and hail fell in a thundery shower early on the 29th.

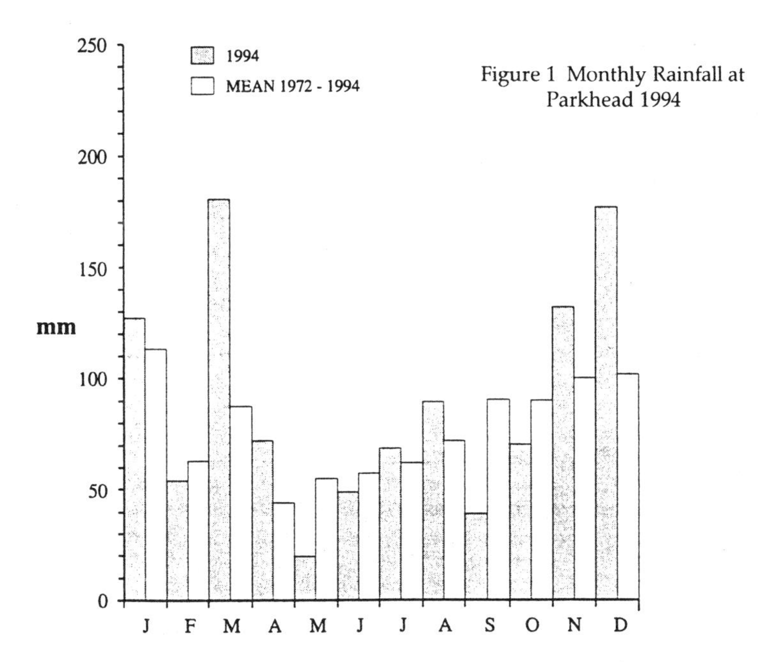

Figure 1 Monthly Rainfall at Parkhead 1994

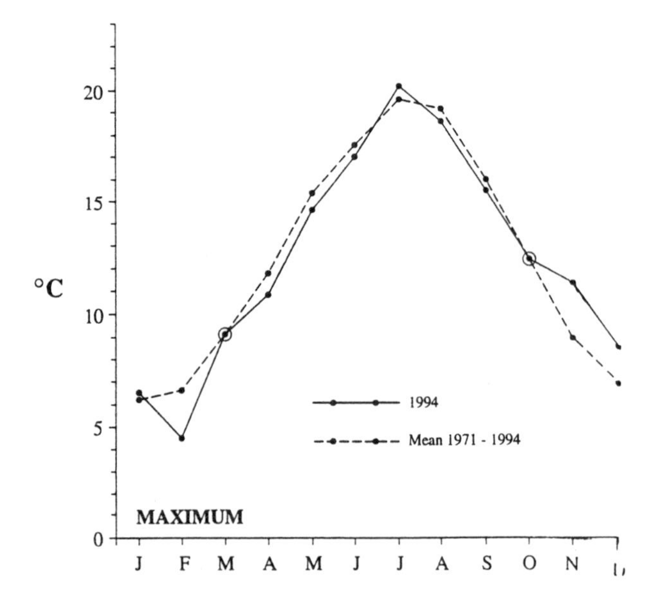

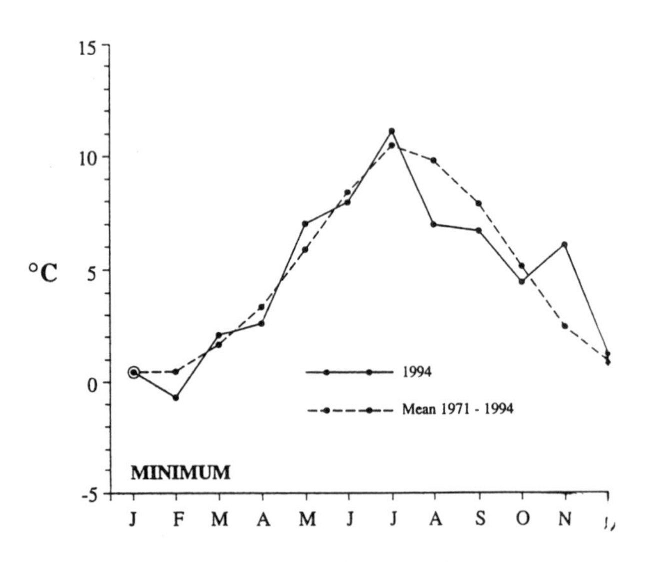

Figure 2 Air Temperatures at Parkhead 1994

NOTES

Gales in Scotland January 23-27th

Severe gales affected Scotland on the 23rd, 24th and 26th of January as deep depressions moved quickly eastwards between Scotland and Iceland. On the 23rd the mean wind speed reached hurricane force (>33ms^{-1}) on Shetland, and gusted to 60ms^{-1} on the 24th when there was widespread damage to buildings and power lines. Gales returned on the 26th, when the wind gusted to 31ms^{-1}. Trees were uprooted and there was some damage to buildings.

Wheeler, D., 1994. 23rd January – a stormy night on Fair Isle. *Climatology Observers Link Bulletin* 285 40.

Dust falls in Bridge of Allan May 2nd and June 1st/2nd

Fine dust, which often originates in the Saharan area of Africa, frequently reaches the British Isles in Tropical continental air and is deposited in rainfall as a red or orange washout. The air is drawn in from the south or south-east as a depression and associated fronts approach the British Isles from the west and when there is a well-developed anticyclone over continental Europe. As rain falls from the advancing fronts it washes out the dust from the atmosphere. On May 2nd and June 1st the amount of dust deposited was relatively small.

Exceptionally mild November

Many climatological stations throughout the British Isles registered the mildest November since their records began, with mean maximum and minimum temperatures 3.0°C above the long-term average. The indications from the Central England Temperature series are that it is necessary to go back to 1818 to find the next warmest November. Places as far north as Cumbria recorded no air frosts during the month. As a result of the mildness there was widespread out-of-season flowering of plants, and early spring growth, and midges seemed to enjoy the warmth. With the prospect of the damaging frosts of January and February yet to come, much of this early leaf growth would be lost, which could lead to eventual delays in spring leaf emergence and blossoming in spring 1995.

	Mean max	Diff.	Mean min	Diff.
Stornoway	11.0	+2.2	6.6	+3.3
Aviemore	10.5	+3.8	4.2	+3.4
Dyce	11.4	+3.1	4.7	+2.9
Leuchars	11.6	+2.9	5.3	+3.0
Abbotsinch	11.9	+3.0	6.7	+4.4
Eskdalemuir	9.8	+2.5	4.8	+3.8
	****	****	***	****
Parkhead	11.7	+2.7	6.2	+3.7

Table 1: Monthly mean temperature for stations in Scotland and difference from the long-term average (Diff.). Temperatures are in degrees Celsius. From *Weather Log* November *1994* Royal Meteorological Society

The underlying cause of the exceptional mildness was the persistence of a cloudy south-westerly airstream from the Azores. Not only was this relatively warm but the persistence of a cloud cover restricted heat loss from the ground at night. It is tempting to attribute this anomalous weather, together with the severe floods in western Europe early in 1995, to global warming but the case for this remains 'not proven'. What is clear is that recent winters have been associated with a more vigorous westerly airflow with its attendant mildness, cloudiness and variability, while cold continental easterly airflow has become a rarer visitor. While this could well be due to a global change in atmospheric pressure systems resulting from global warming, it could also be a part of the natural variability inherent in the complex relationship between atmosphere and ocean.

Floods in Strathclyde Region December 10-13th

Rain entered Strathclyde Region from the south-west by 22.00 on Friday 9th December and over the following 54hrs up to 120mm had fallen over the Glasgow area, of which more than 70mm fell on the 10th, which was a record 24hr total for Glasgow Airport. A warm front approached Scotland in the early hours of the 10th and by 06.00 heavy continuous rain was falling in a freshening south-westerly wind, a cocktail which persisted unabated until the early hours of the 12th. The band of rain remained almost stationary over Strathclyde and was maintained by a supply of warm and very moist air from the south-west. The rain-shadow effect in the south-westerly wind was very marked, the Forth Valley receiving a little over 50% of the total received by Glasgow, although even this was sufficient to cause flooding.

The heavy rain hit an area with a long history of flooding, and warnings were issued by the police late on the 10th. By the early hours of the 11th, the Cart, Kelvin and Irvine had overflowed their banks and there was widespread flooding in Kirkintilloch, Irvine, Paisley, Johnstone and Beith. Many residents were forced to seek temporary accommodation in church halls and schools, and more than 600 were homeless for at least two nights. Early estimates of claims on insurance policies appear to suggest that the cost of the flood may run into many millions of pounds, added to which are the personal losses incurred by those residents who were not covered by insurance.

Date	Time	Rainfall (mm)	Total (mm)
9th	0900 – 2100	X	X
	2100 – 0900	9	9
10th	0900 – 2100	35	44
	2100 – 0900	37	81
11th	0900 – 2100	30	111
	2100 – 0900	7	118
12th	0900 – 2100	2	120
	2100 – 0900	X	120

Table 2: Rainfall recorded at Glasgow Airport between December 9th and 12th 1994
From *Daily Weather Summary*, London Weather Centre

Thousands of homes were left without electricity and many major roads were blocked by flood water. Parts of the tunnel carrying ScotRail's Argyle Line beneath Glasgow city centre were under 10ft of water (*Railnews* February 1995) and it would be several months before services were restored. An early-morning commuter train was abandonned by its passengers at Glasgow Central Low Level as the flood waters rose. Hundreds of tons of silt, sludge and debris were washed into the tunnel. As was the case with the Chichester flood in January, the expansion of the urban area of Glasgow was considered to have made a major contribution to the severity of the flooding.

Material for this brief report has been drawn from accounts published in the *Herald* and the *Scotsman*.

Figure 3 Annual precipitation (mm) over Scotland 1757-1992 (A) Individual values (B) ten-year running mean. (From Smith K Precipitation over Scotland, 1757-1992: some aspects of temporal variability *International Journal of Climatology* 15, 543-556)

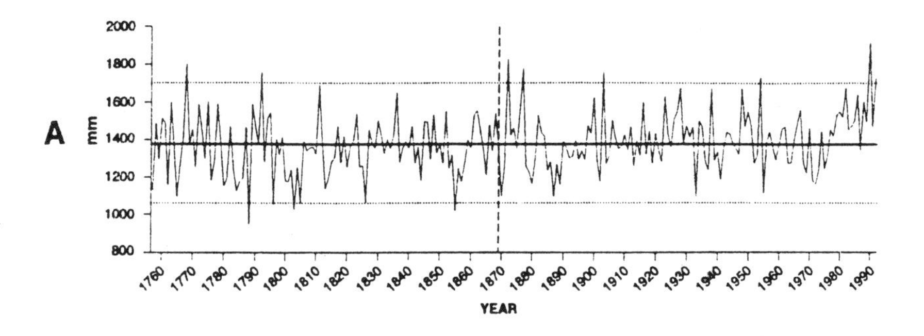

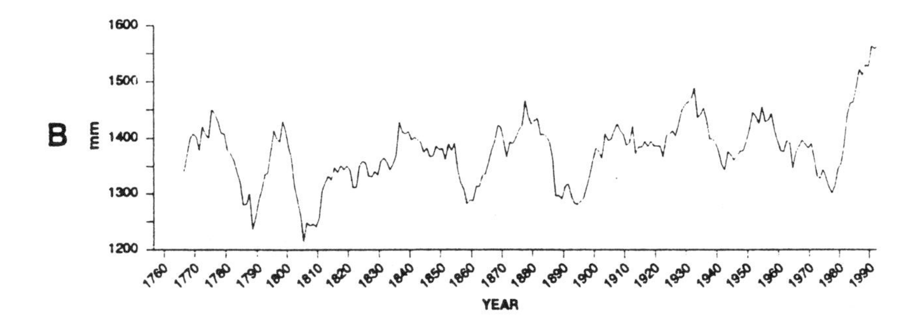

Temporal variability in precipitation in Scotland

A 236-year time series (1757-1992) of monthly areal average precipitation for Scotland (Figure 3) has been produced using records compiled by the Met Office. The series has been examined for fluctuations and extreme values, with particular reference to observed precipitation increases over the last two decades. There has been a recent trend towards higher winter precipitation.

Spatial and temporal variation in snow-cover in the Scottish uplands

The distribution of snow-cover in the Scottish uplands has a considerable bearing on the ecology of these areas in addition to being a major influence on the viability of the skiing industry. Recent winters have shown a change from continental easterly to milder and more variable westerly weather patterns which affects the amount, duration, and character of snowfall. The spatial distribution of snowfall in upland areas is a result of the operation of several factors including altitude and topographic shelter, in addition to the direction of movement of snow-bearing weather systems. The relationship between snow accumulation and altitude is difficult to define because of a basic shortage of data. Values for the frequency of days on which snow is seen to be lying are available for most climatological stations but the majority of these lie at elevations below 400m. Estimates of snow cover duration for higher altitudes must, therefore, use some form of predictive model based on data from much lower altitudes. Topographic variation operates directly on the spatial variability of snow accumulation through its effect on the shelter-windspeed relationship. The location of persistent snow patches into late spring and early summer is a result of a complex balance between antecedent accumulations and ablation rates, the latter being affected in large measure by aspect.

Harrison, S. J., Sydes, C., Mordaunt, C. and Dawber, M. Changes in the snow climate of the Scottish mountains and their effect on alpine plant communities (in preparation).

Climate of Central Scotland

An analysis of available climatological data for Central Region has been published as a contribution to a wider study of Central Scotland. The report considers air temperature, rainfall, sunshine, frost, fog and wind speed and direction. A brief description of climatic conditions in the Ochil Hills has also been published.

Harrison, S. J. 1994. Climate in: Corbett L. (Ed) Central Scotland – land, wildlife, people. Forth Naturalist & Historian.

Harrison, S. J. 1994. Climate/Weather In: Corbett L., Roy E. K. and Snaddon, R. C. The Ochil Hills. Forth Naturalist & Historian/Clackmannanshire Field Studies Society.

Acknowledgment

This paper is a summary of the more comprehensive report which is published in the Annual Climatological Bulletin No.16 of the University of Stirling, copies of which can be purchased from Climate Services in the Department of Environmental Science.

A BATHYMETRIC RESURVEY OF THE LAKE OF MENTEITH

Silke F. K. Wewetzer, University of St Andrews

Abstract

A bathymetric survey of the Lake of Menteith was undertaken in June 1992 by means of recording echo-sounding and side-scan sonar techniques coupled with position fixing using the Global Positioning System (GPS). This resurvey with modern equipment largely confirms the earlier findings of Murray and Pullar in 1900, but suggests that sediment infill of up to 0.7 m has taken place in the interim. Moreover, it has served to locate what is interpreted as the submerged remains of a second crannog (lake dwelling), hitherto unrecognised in the lake.

Introduction and setting

The Lake of Menteith is situated in central Scotland where it forms part of the drainage network of the River Forth. Located at 56°10'N, 4°17'W between the Trossachs and Stirling, the lowland water body lies between the Highland Boundary Fault to the north and the Ochil Fault to the south in a broad plain of clays and peat mosses. Like most of the Scottish freshwater lochs it has been formed by the effects of Pleistocene glaciation. An extensive area of moundy fluvioglacial and alluvial sands occurs around the lake and in the form of a spit-like body projecting northwards from the southern shore. Within these deposits the lake occupies a cup-like depression to the west of the Menteith Moraine (Browne 1977). It has been suggested that the Menteith Moraine is a composite feature, only part of which is a true moraine associated with the Loch Lomond Stadial (Laxton, 1984). The depression is interpreted as a large kettle-hole (George 1974), or rather as a group of closely-spaced kettle-holes. Due to its morphometry the lake is considered to be predisposed towards eutrophic conditions (Fozzard and Marsden 1990). The lake has a maximum length of 1.6 miles (2.57 km), a mean breadth of 0.64 miles (1.02 km), a water surface area of 1.02 sq. miles (2.64 km^2) and it drains a catchment area of 6.35 square miles (16.45 km^2) (Maulood and Boney 1981).

The Island of Inchmahome, the largest of the three in the lake, has the important 13th century priory ruin which, for a time, was a refuge for the infant Mary Queen of Scots. This attracts many visitors in summer months when a small ferry service to Inchmahome operates from just south of Port of Menteith (Figure 1). Another main attraction during the summer months is trout fishing. The fish are reared in ponds adjacent to the lake and in floating cages in the north west corner of the lake.

Previous bathymetric survey

At the turn of the century systematic charting of the Scottish freshwater lochs began under the direction of Sir John Murray and Frederick Pullar. Duck

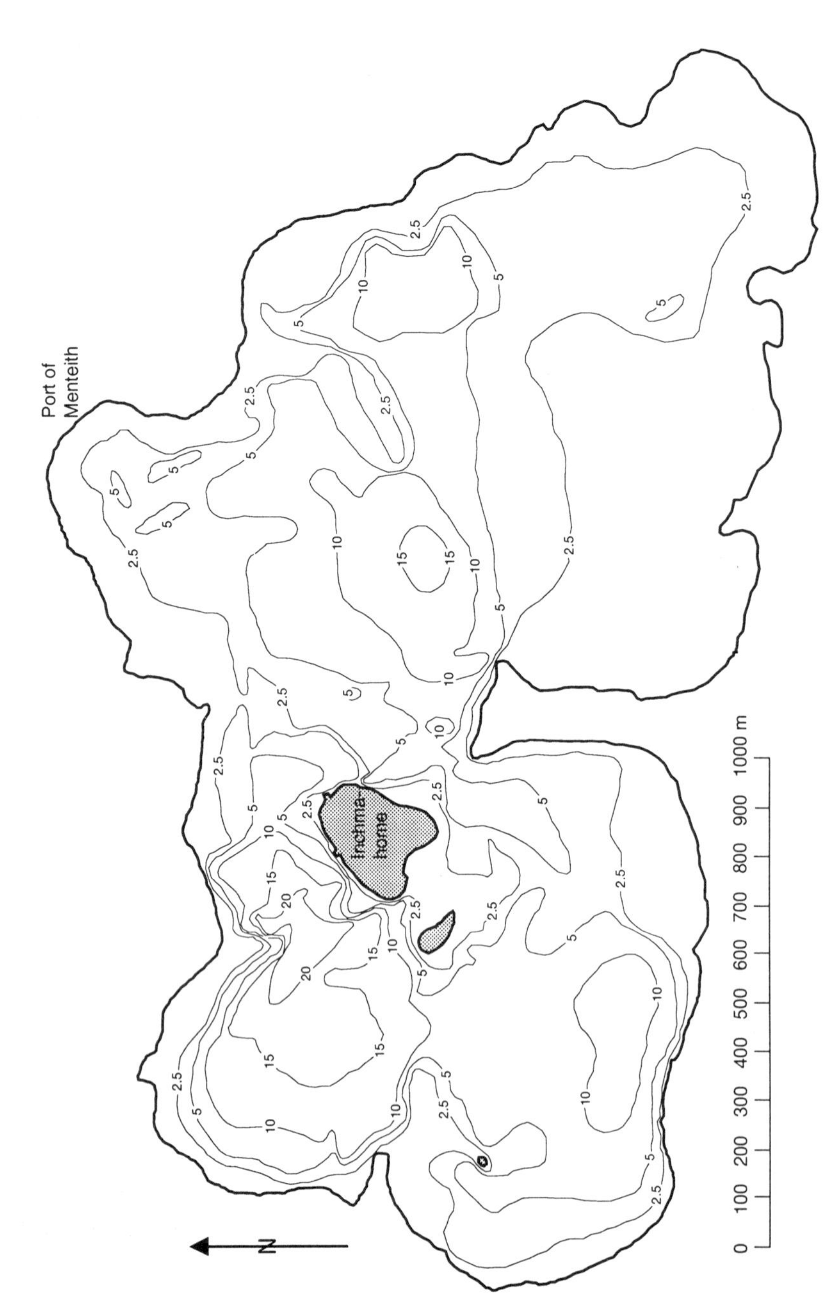

Figure 1 Bathymetric chart of the Lake of Menteith

(1990) gives a brief history of this work, the untimely death of Pullar, and his father's subsequent role in supporting the enterprise. Between 1897 and 1909, a total of 562 lochs were surveyed and many of the results published in several journals before the Challenger Office in Edinburgh collated all the charts and descriptions of the lochs in six volumes (Murray and Pullar 1910).

The Murray and Pullar surveys were conducted from rowing boats using the lead-line method for determining water depth. This method utilises a lead-lining recorder, in which the sounding line runs through a winch system which records on dials the length paid out. The accuracy of the method depends essentially on two factors which can over-estimate depth:

1. Wind action may cause the boat to drift so that the sounding line falls at an angle through the water column.

2. The lead weight may penetrate into soft bed sediments for an unknown distance before resistance is detected by the remote surveyor.

The method of determining the position of the soundings relied on a certain number of pulls of the oars made between two well-defined points on each side of the loch. The positions of the soundings were then evenly spaced along the line of traverse and plotted onto a 1: 10,560 scale Ordnance Survey map.

During the Murray and Pullar survey of the Lake of Menteith in 1900, a total of 375 depth soundings were made along 34 traverses totalling a length of approximately 14.53 km. According to the area of the lake this results in a ratio of one sounding per 7,040 m^2. Thus, areally small but important features may have been missed in the gaps between the survey lines. The resultant bathymetric chart was published at a scale of 1:21,120 or 3 inches to 1 mile (0.21 km to 1 cm) with isobaths constructed at 10, 25, 50 and 75 feet (3.05, 7.6, 15.2 and 22.9 m) below the water surface level.

At the time of the Murray and Pullar survey the water surface of the lake was 55 feet (16.76 m) above sea level, relative to the contemporary datum of mean sea level at Liverpool. This is equivalent to 55.5 feet (16.92 m) above the modern Ordnance Datum (OD), Newlyn. Since the maximum depth recorded was 77 feet, a small portion of the water body was found to be below sea level. The bathymetric chart shows that the lake bottom is apparently very irregular. It is generally a shallow water body incorporating two basins in its eastern part, which were found to extend to depths of 46 and 49 feet. An area of much deeper water, today known as the 'deep hole', was discovered north west of Inchmahome, with a maximum depth of 77 feet (23.47 m). A fourth basin, located to the south west of Inchmahome is shown to have extended to a depth of 49 feet. The 10 feet isobath in the Murray and Pullar chart approximately follows the trend of the shoreline of the loch but is shifted away from the southern and south eastern margins due to the outward growth of reed beds. In the extreme north eastern embayment of the lake, close to Port of Menteith, a submerged crannog was identified, covered by only four feet of water (Murray and Pullar 1910). A crannog is defined as a fortified island in a lake, partly natural and partly artificial (Morrison, 1985).

Resurvey methods

Since the work of Murray and Pullar few attempts to resurvey individual freshwater lochs have been made (e.g. Duck and McManus, 1985; Lowe et al. 1991a, b). At least one attempt to produce a new bathymetric chart of the Lake of Menteith was made in the 1940s, but the results have not been published.

In the intervening decades hydrographic surveying techniques have advanced considerably. The lead-line method is now superseded by electronic echo-sounding devices which work on a range of frequencies and yield continuous records of water depth beneath a motor-propelled survey vessel. Modern radio fixing apparatus or the Global Positioning System (GPS) provide a far better accuracy than dead reckoning.

This bathymetrical resurvey of the Lake of Menteith was conducted in June 1992 using a Lowrance (Model X15M, 192 kHz) recording echo-sounder operating from the 20 foot outboard propelled GRP boat, RV Mya of the Tay Estuary Research Centre. An echo-sounder does not provide a direct measurement of water depth (McQuillin and Ardus 1977) but computes the time taken for an acoustic pulse from a transducer on the survey vessel to reach the sea or lake bed and be reflected back. This two-way travel time is then converted to a measure of water depth for a known velocity of sound in either fresh or salt water (Hooper 1979). The echo-sounder record is built up by a series of sweeps of a stylus across recording paper and depicts a continuous profile of the level of the bed beneath the moving survey vessel. The echo-sounder trace is periodically marked with lines (event marks) which correspond to simultaneously recorded fixes of the vessel's position (McQuillin and Ardus 1977).

Position-fixing is necessary to compile observations made at different sites into maps/charts showing their correct spatial relationship (op cit). The GPS deployed in this survey, depends on the reception of signals from a group of satellites which circle the earth twice daily in a fixed orbit. To obtain a position fix the GPS receiver needs to locate at least three satellites for a 2-dimensional fix and uses the time of transmission and reception of the signals to calculate the distance and the orbital position of the satellites in relation to the receiver. This information allows the receiver to compute its position on the earth's surface in terms of latitude and longitude (Magellan Systems Corporation 1990).

During the June 1992 survey 37 traverses were completed totalling a length of 30.15 km and incorporating 470 GPS fixes. Since the echo-sounder records are continuous a far better coverage was achieved compared with the point observations of the lead-line method. However, in order to ascertain that small features of the lake bed had not been missed as a result of their spacing , side-scan sonar was employed as a fill-in between the echo-sounder track lines.

Side-scan sonar systems are similar to echo-sounders in that they work on the principle of reflection of sound from the bed. However, unlike the conical beam of sound emitted vertically downwards by an echo-sounder, that of the side-scan sonar has a narrow horizontal beam angle (<2°) and a wide vertical beam angle (>20°). Modern instruments comprise two sound sources, housed in a towfish transducer, which emit sound energy in opposite directions through the water column. By this means a swathe beam coverage of the bed is achieved. For this investigation such a dual channel instrument (Klein Hydroscan, Model 401, operating frequency 400 kHz) with a towfish type transducer was employed using a scanning range of 75 m per channel (i.e. to either side of the towfish). The resultant acoustic image of the bed, or sonograph, is a slightly distorted plan view of the shape and texture of the surface of the lake floor (Belderson et al. 1972). A sonograph consists basically of a sheet of paper marked by shades of varying tonal intensity (backscatter levels) depending on both the relief (positive or negative) of underwater bedforms (natural and anthropogenic) as well as on the density of the bed sediments. For further details of this method the reader is referred to McQuillin and Ardus (1977) and Fish and Carr (1990).

For the production of the bathymetric chart the GPS fixes corresponding with the event marks on the echo-sounder traces were plotted onto a 1:10,000 scale map by means of an electronic plotter and then inter-connected to show the traverse lines. The depth value measured for each position fix on the echo-sounder records was transferred onto the map as well as important changes in depths between position fixes. Intermediate specified depth values (2.5 m, 5.0 m, 10.0 m, 15.0 m and 20.0 m), often between fixes, were marked onto an overlay and then joined to form contour lines thereby producing the bathymetric chart. This was then checked against the sonographs from the side-scan sonar survey in order to determine whether or not significant positive and negative relief features had been missed by the echo-sounding and, if so, appropriate modifications were made to the isobaths.

New bathymetric chart

The new bathymetric chart of the Lake of Menteith is shown in Figure 1. The isobaths are constructed relative to a water level of 16.32 m above OD, Newlyn (this was levelled from a bench mark at the church in Port of Menteith at the time of survey, 2 and 3 June, 1992). Thus, the water level when Murray and Pullar's 1900 survey was carried out (using sea-level datum, Liverpool) was 0.60 m higher than during the June 1992 survey. This must be taken into account should comparisons of water depth be made.

General comparison of the results of the two bathymetric surveys reveals an overall similarity. The recent study has confirmed that the bottom of the lake is certainly very irregular consisting essentially of four basins, each greater than 10 m in depth, inter-connected by areas of shallower water. In order to describe the bathymetry, it is convenient to divide the lake into halves by means of a north-south line through its narrowest point east of Inchmahome. These will be referred to as the eastern and western halves.

The eastern half of the lake is mainly shallow with two basins, eastern and western, having greatest depths of 13.8 m and 16.2 m respectively. The western half shows an asymmetrical bottom with the largest and deepest basin, the so-called 'deep hole' which extends to the maximum recorded depth of 22.3 m, to the north west of Inchmahome. A shallower basin, 14.1 m in greatest depth, occupies the south-west corner of the lake. The 2.5 m isobath approximately follows the shoreline of the lake like the 10 feet contour line of Murray and Pullar's chart. In the north-east corner of the lake three small depressions, with depths of more than 5 m, were found in an area with general depths of around 3 m. One similar depression was found in the southeast corner but none in the western half of the lake (Figure 1).

Side-scan sonar survey

The side-scan sonographs enabled the recognition of changes in sediment type on the lake bed from relatively coarse sands, gravels and cobbles at the margins and around the islands to finer muds in the deeper waters. Grab samples of the 'offshore deposits' were collected to calibrate the sonographs. Localised patches of boulders were also identified. It is not known whether these are natural or reflect man's former activities in the lake.

Perhaps the most interesting feature recorded in this survey was a strong reflection indicative of an approximately circular body in plan, with a diameter of 12 m, found off the north-eastern shore of Inchmahome (Figure 2). By analogy with the size, shape and tonal intensity of the reflection obtained from the 'known' crannog (Figure 3) close to Port of Menteith, indicated on Murray and Pullar's chart, it is suggested that this body, covered by less than 5 m of water at the time of survey, is also a submerged crannog, hitherto unrecognised. However, in order to test this hypothesis, direct observations by archaeological divers are required.

Discussion

It is difficult to make meaningful comparisons between the results of surveys which have been conducted using such different surveying methods affording differing degrees of positional and bathymetric accuracy. Indeed it is almost impossible to establish the location of pairs of depth measurements which relate precisely to the same point in the lake. However, several virtually coincident pairs of depth measurements have been determined and, when corrections are applied to take account of the different water levels, it is possible to make some crude comparisons of depth.

In general terms the lake is now shallower than in 1900. In the 'deep hole' there appears to have been between 0.3 and 0.7 m of sediment accretion during the period between surveys. Suggestions of larger thicknesses of localised sedimentation (up to 2 m) are possible due to positional inaccuracies but could be the result of sediment focusing and downslope slumping into this deep basin. In the other basins of the lake amounts of infill ranging in thickness from zero to 0.7 m are indicated. In the extensive south-eastern shallows, what appears as infill due to sedimentation is likely to be, at least in part, the result of the advance of aquatic macrophyte vegetation into the water body. These comparisons of water depth suggest that rates of sedimentation in the Lake of Menteith average between zero (i.e. undetectable rate of infill) and 7-8 mm/year. The upper limit is considerably higher than the rate of 1.5-2 mm/year determined in the deep water, rock basin Loch Earn, (Duck 1987). However, it must be re-emphasised that these figures should be treated with some caution owing to the problems inherent in comparing the two sets of bathymetric data.

Acknowledgements

The author wishes to express her thanks to Dr Duck for his continuous support, to Mr Lorimer, helmsman of the survey vessel, to Prof McManus for suggesting this research project and to Mr Nairn for access permission.

References and Further Reading

BELDERSON, R. H., KENYON, N. H., STRIDE, A. H. and STUBBS, A. R. 1972. *Sonographs of the sea floor.* A picture atlas. Elsevier, Amsterdam, 183 pp.

BROWNE, M. A. E. 1977. Sand and gravel resources of the Central Region, Scotland. *Report of the Institute of Geological Sciences*, No. 77/9, 27 pp.

DUCK, R. W. 1987. Aspects of physical processes of sedimentation in Loch Earn. *In* Gardiner, V. (Ed.), International Geomorphology, 801-821, John Wiley, Chichester.

DUCK, R. W. 1990. Charting of Scotland's lochs. *Forth Naturalist and Historian* 13, 25-30.

DUCK, R.W. and McMANUS, J. 1985. Bathymetric charts of ten Scottish Lochs. *Tay Estuary Research Centre Report* 9, 31 pp.

FISH, J. P. and CARR, H. A. 1990. Sound underwater images. American Underwater Search and Survey Limited, Cataumet, Massachusetts, U. S. A., 188 pp.

FOZZARD, I. and MARSDEN, M. 1990. The Lake of Menteith, some aspects of its ecology. *The Scottish Naturalist* 102, 97-129.

GEORGE, T. N. 1974. p43 in The Stirling Region. ed. Timms. University of Stirling, and BROWNE et al 1994. p13 in Central Scotland – Land, Wildlife, People. Forth Naturalist and Historian.

HOOPER, D. J. 1979. Hydrographic surveying. *In* Dyer, K. R. (Ed.), Estuarine hydrography and sedimentation, 41-56, Cambridge University Press.

LAXTON, J. L. 1984. The occurrence of possible Late-glacial estuarine deposits at levels above the Carse Clay west of Stirling. *Scottish Journal of Geology* 20, 107-114.

LOWE, P. A., DUCK, R. W. and McMANUS, J. 1991a. Bathymetric charts of three south east Grampian lochs. *Tay Estuary Research Centre Report* 10, 16 pp.

LOWE, P.A., DUCK, R. W. and McMANUS, J. 1991b. A bathymetric reappraisal of Loch Muick, Aberdeenshire. *Scottish Geographical Magazine* 107, 110-115.

McQUILLIN, R. and ARDUS, D. A. 1977. Exploring the geology of shelf seas. Graham & Trotman, London, 234 pp.

MAGELLAN SYSTEMS CORPORATION 1990. Magellan NAV1000PLUS ™User Guide, 141 pp.

MAULOOD, B. K.. and BONEY, A. D. 1981. Phytoplankton ecology of the Lake of Menteith, Scotland. *Hydrobiologia* 79, 179-186.

MORRISON, I. A. 1985. Landscape with lake dwellings. The crannogs of Scotland, Edinburgh University Press, 117 pp.

MURRAY, Sir J. and PULLAR, L. 1910. Bathymetrical survey of the Scottish Freshwater Lochs. Challenger Office, Edinburgh, 6 Volumes.

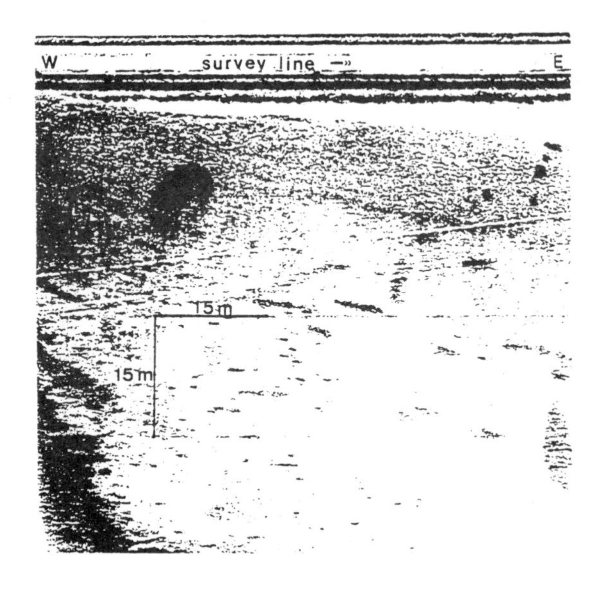

Figure 2 Previously unrecognised feature comparable with the submerged crannog shown in Figure 3

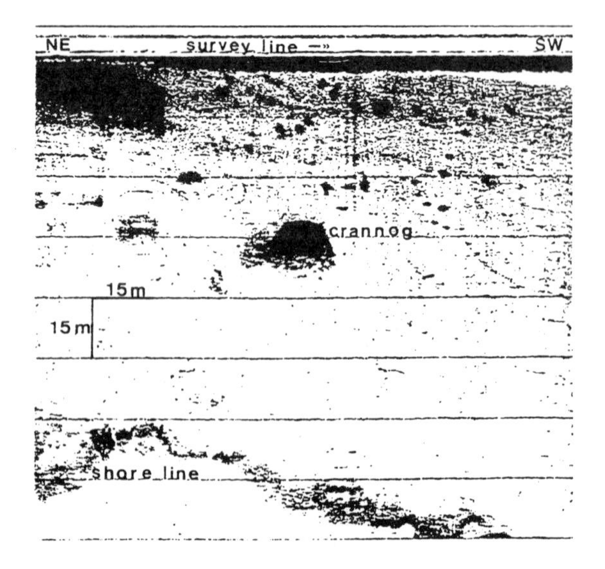

Figure 3 The 'known' crannog close to Port of Menteith detected by side-scan sonar.

FORTH AREA BIRD REPORT 1994

C J Henty
University of Stirling

This report is compiled from a larger archive of records submitted to the local recorder under the national scheme organised by the Scottish Ornithologists Club. The area covered by the report comprises the Districts of Falkirk and Clackmannan together with Stirling District excluding Loch Lomondside and other parts of the Clyde drainage basin. Records from Carron Valley may be published both here and in the report on Clyde birds. The political/administrative boundaries are in a state of flux so no large alterations have been made in the way records are divided among the sub-regions. The inland part of Falkirk District continues to receive reasonable attention, the extensive and often inaccessable hill area in the north of our area has had only sporadic coverage.

The recent major book covering the birds of our area *Central Scotland (Land-Wildlife-People)*, 1994, published by Forth Naturalist and Historian, is now available at a bargain price of £5 and contains a chapter reviewing the status of the birds of Central Region. The major systematic account of local breeding birds is still a (small) part of *The New Atlas of Breeding Birds in Britain and Ireland* British Trust for Ornithology, 1993.

The Scottish Ornithologists Club (SOC) has pressed for a more systematic vetting of records of species that are unusual locally, this area now has an informal committee of five - C. Henty (Recorder), W. Brackenridge (Dep. Recorder), J. Crook (local SOC rep), A. Blair and D. Thorogood. The judging of national UK or Scottish rarities continues as before, but we are producing for the upper Forth a list of species that are scarce locally and where the records need to be supported by either a full description or sufficient evidence to remove any reasonable doubt. This list and an explanation of the situation will be available by the end of the year - there is no need for any alarm since it will only affect a small percentage of records and most contributors will not be concerned at all.

The 1994 weather was characterised by a cold spell in February, heavy rain and floods in March, a cloudy summer and a wet and mild end to the year. January and February were generally unsettled and wet with a short spell of snow at the end of January and much more prolonged cold weather through mid and late February. March was windy and exceptionally wet with a brief cold snap in the third week. April was cold with some snow at first but later gave some sunny weather whilst May was markedly dry though often cool. The summer was generally cool and cloudy leading to a dry September and the first frost in early October, though the rest of that month had very varied conditions. November was very wet and markedly milder than usual, this pattern continued in December except for some brief frosty and snowy spells.

Notable records for this year include Ruddy Shelduck on the estuary (a new addition to the area list provided it is accepted by British Birds Record Committee (BBRC), and with some reservation about the possibility of escapes) and Long-tailed Skuas, only the second occurrence. I am indebted to D. Thorogood for producing an armchair addition to the list by detecting a 1977 record of Water Pipit at Kinneil - since then it has been deemed a full species, not lumped with Rock Pipit, and Kinneil has been shifted from West Lothian to Falkirk District. Although wintering waders were in good numbers the autumn passage of the scarcer waders was once again generally poor. There has been a welcome increase in Stonechat records suggesting that this species is at last recovering after years of low population. The Lesser Whitethroat that sang this year (1994) from a bank of Hawthorn and Elder in Stirling reappeared in 1995, but still had no apparent success in attracting a mate. It is peculiarly difficult to make useful observations on many common resident species, especially concerning their breeding abundance; Hedgesparrows and Treecreepers are notable cases. Some comments on the abundance of common resident species have been made, quoting data on records per kilometre of transect or per hour; transects mean that birds have been recorded systematically along a particular route, counts usually being repeated on several dates. For less common species I can sometimes mention data in terms of the numbers of pairs or apparently occupied territories for particular locations. For many species the records sent in are very unrepresentative of their general distribution, this applies particularly to very common species or to those that are secretive or breed in inaccessable places. Readers can consult the Check List published in the *Forth Naturalist and Historian* vol 15, but in addition I have in this report put, after the species name, a coded summary of general distribution.

B - Breeding status, widespread (in more than five 10 km squares)
b - " " , local, scarce (in fewer than five 10 km squares)
W - Winter status, widespread or often in groups of more than ten.
w - " " , local, scarce (local and usually fewer than ten in a group)
P - Passage (used when species is usually absent in winter, *P* or *p* used for widespread or local as in winter status)
S or *s* - a few species are present in summer but do not normally breed.

Thus *BW* would be appropriate for Robin, *B* for Swallow, *p* for Ruff and *SW* for Cormorant. No status letter is used if a species occurs less than every other year. Square brackets [ ] at one entry means 'escaped from captivity'.

An asterix (*) in front of the species name means that all records received have been quoted. A new series of Breeding Bird Surveys has been set up by the British trust for Ornithology, these are based on transects in one kilometre squares. A number of these are active in the area and I hope in the future to include a yearly account of their results.

For several species of waders and duck more information has been received than can be sensibly reported in full detail. In these cases I have mentioned the more striking individual records and summarised the rest for each month or half-month as the minimum number of birds that can reasonably account for the records, this means adding up the maximum numbers recorded for what I take to be distinct localities. These "Area summaries" clearly have limitations, underestimating when an important locality has not been visited and overestimating if the same flock has been reported from two places that I have assumed to be separate; however, this is the best way of giving a more systematic description of the seasonal pattern of occurrence. A fresh feature is an account of the main results of the national wildfowl counts Wildfowl and Estuary Bird Survey (WEBS). The new organiser for the inland waters, Neil Bielby, has made available a summary of the results for the winter 1994-1995 and we hope to produce a fuller version for future winters; suggestions about the presentation of this information would be welcomed.

This report has been produced under considerable time pressure and the editor acknowledges that many of the species accounts would be improved if there were more explanation of the raw results. One observer who visited Glen Lochay in May did not add a name to record sheet - this got separated from any covering note so the records are unattributed, sorry !

The following abbreviations have been used: AoT - apparently occupied territory, BoA - Bridge of Allan, c/n - clutch of n eggs, CP - Country Park, F - Female, GP - gravel pit, J - juvenile, L. - Loch, NR - Nature Reserve, M - Male, ON - on nest, Res - Reservoir, SP - summer plumage, V - Valley, WG - Wildlife Garden, Y - young.

This report has been compiled from records submitted by: The late K Anderson, M V Bell, N Bielby, Birdline Scotland, A Blair, W R Brackenridge, W Brown, D M Bryant, M Callan, H E M Dott, A Fairweather, D Fotheringham, S Harley, B Hay, C J Henty, F Henderson, A Hogg, B Howe (BH), B Hutcheon (BHc), E A Jardine, D&R Jones, C McGuigan, A Maciver, A K McNeil, D & M Matthews, J Mitchell, G Owens, D Orr-Ewing, D J Price, H Robb, S Sankey, R Shand, M Steward (Forest Enterprise), P Stirling-Aird, R&A Summers(RSm), D Thorogood, J Towill, M Trubridge, J Wheeler.

Thanks are due to the Deputy Recorder, W.R.Brackenridge, for assistance and advice on records, to Dr S.J.Harrison for a copy of the Annual Climatological Bulletin (1994) and to Dr M.V.Bell for assessing the counts of geese.

SYSTEMATIC LIST

Codes - F and C indicate records from Falkirk and Clackmannan Districts, S and SWP those from one time Stirlingshire and south-west Perthshire parts of Stirling District.

RED-THROATED DIVER *Gavia stellata (b,w)*

22 on Forth Estuary 13 Feb (DMB)

F Higgins Neuk: 1 on 26 Feb, 5 on 12 Mar (DF). 1 Skinflats 29 Oct (GO).

S 2 Carron V Res 7 May (AKM).

SWP 1 Lake of Menteith 14 Apr (BHc). 2 Loch A on 26 May & 1 on 2 Jun. Loch E- pr attempted but failed, poss mink (MT).
1 L.Drunkie 21 Jun (SS).

BLACK-THROATED DIVER *Gavia arctica (b,w)*

F 1 Bo'ness 24 Feb & 2 Mar (DMB DOE).

C 2 Gartmorn Feb-Mar (MC).

SWP Loch A: Pr 26 Mar-7 Jun, 3 on 7 Apr; pr 19-30 Jun & incubation from 21 Jun, heavy rain flooded nest by 25 Jun; 3 on 5 Jul, 4 on 7 Aug & 1 on 3 Sept. Loch F: Pr raised 1 Y (MT).

LITTLE GREBE *Tachybaptus ruficollis (B,w)*

F 4 Grangemouth Docks 6 Nov (MVB).

C 6 pairs Gartmorn, only 1 pr reared 3Y, birds left in late June prob due to algal bloom (MC), 15 on 10 Sep & 3 on 16 Nov (NB).

S 5 on Forth at Drip Camp 26 Feb. Airthrey: 5 by 25 Mar, poor breeding with 3 pr rearing 1+2Y; 9 on 5 Sep, 1 in mid Dec (MVB). Pr Carron V Res 15 Jul (CJH).

SWP 1 Ashfield 19 Oct (WRB). 1 W.Braeleny Res 26 Jun (SS).
2 Prs L.Watston 10 Apr, Ad+y on 9 Jul (CJH). 9 L.Voil 6 Sep & 2 on 14 Dec, up to four on 14 Dec at L.Lubnaig, L.Doine, L.Dochart. 1 Blairdrummond 23 Dec (NB). (Frequency of Dec records may reflect mild weather, Ed).

GREAT CRESTED GREBE *Podiceps cristatus (b,W)*

Forth Estuary 573 on 13 Feb (DMB).

F 130 Bo'ness 30 Mar (DMB), 20 Blackness 15 Jan (DT). 20 Blackness 15 Jan, 3 Blackness 23 Feb, 5 on 7 Aug (CJH).
Kinneil: 51 on 15 Jan; 15 on 9 Jul & 24 on 31st; max 70 through Aug; max 100 through Sep; 11 on 24 Oct, 68 on 27 Nov, 2 on 18 Dec (AB DMB MVB CJH AMcI DT). 2 Higgins Neuk 26 Feb & 1 on 18 Sep (DF).

C 1 pair Gartmorn, failed due to Coot predation (MC), 14 on 21 Oct & 5 on 16 Nov (NB).

S Carron V Res: 2 on 10 Mar & 4 on 23rd, 12 on 10 Jul, 6 on 8 Oct & 5 on 6 Nov (NB BHc DT). 5 pairs but no Y reared due to low water (AKM).

SWP 4 Lake of Menteith 18 Mar, 2 on 10 Apr & 10 on 16th, 3+2Y 19 Sep, 1 on 19 Dec (NB AM DT). 2 L.Watston 10 Apr, 1 on 15 May & 9 Jul (CJH).
1 Blairdrummond GP 10 Apr & 15 May, 3 on 9 Jul, 2 (1 ON) 25 Aug, 2+2Y on 5 Oct (NB CJH).

SLAVONIAN GREBE *Podiceps auritus*

S Carron V. Res: 1 in SP 9 Apr to 8 Aug (AKM), tried to keep company with GCG (CJH EAJ DT). (What was presumably the same bird was present through July 1993 (AKM). This record was not published in these reports for security reasons but did appear in full in Clyde Birds. It has not reappeared in 1995, so there are now no grounds for suppressing the record Ed).

FULMAR *Fulmarus glacialis (p)*

F 1 Kinneil 26 Feb, 3 on 4 Sept (AB DT). 12 ->W Higgins Neuk 22 Aug (DF).

GANNET *Sula bassana (p)*

F 1 immature Skinflats on 11 Oct - walking on mudflats with goose flock (GO).

CORMORANT *Phalacrocorax carbo (S,W)*

Forth Estuary: 236 on 13 Feb (DMB)

F Skinflats max 110 on 8 Jan, 121 on 13 Feb & 210 on 14 Dec (MVB WRB).

C S.Alloa roost; 133 on 6 Nov & 146 on 4 Dec (MVB). 65 Kennetpans 15 Jan (DT). 36 Gartmorn 21 Oct (NB).1 on Devon at Tillicoultry 16 Feb (CJH).

S 5 Craigforth 5 Mar & Airthrey on 14th (MVB DT). 14 Carron V Res 6 Nov & 12 on 4 Dec (NB). 1 on Forth at Frew 10 Jan & 2 Feb (CJH).

SWP 15 Lake of Menteith 25 Mar, 5 & 14 Apr, 17 on 17 Oct (NB BHc DT). 1 L.Watston 31 Jul (CJH). 3 L.Voil 7 Feb (DOE).

SHAG *Phalacrocorax aristotelis (w)*

F 1 dead at Kinneil 26 Feb (DT). 2 Ad, long dead, Airth shore 13 Apr (CJH).

GREY HERON *Ardea cinerea (B,W)*

F 10-15 nests in Spruce plantation at Airth 5 Jun (DMB). 7 Higgins Neuk 22 Aug & 11 on 18 Sep (DF). Max Skinflats 6 on 16 Apr & 7 on 16 & 23 Jul, 9 on 14 Dec (AB MVB GO).

C 4 nests Gartmorn (MC). 23 Alloa Inch 6 Nov (MVB).

SWP 11 used nests Blairdrummond (Nyadd) 23 May. 8 L.Venachar 31 Jul (CJH). 9 Lecropt 5 Feb (MVB).

MUTE SWAN *Cygnus olor (B,W)*

F Jupiter WLG - Pr with 3J on 8 Jan, pr alone on 24th (WRB). Max 5 Skinflats 7 Jan, 2 in Oct-Nov (AB GO). 9 on Union Canal Falkirk 27 May (big increase in last year AMcl), 6 Prs Almond-Bonnybridge all successful, 24Y in Jun; Pr Grangemouth Docks, no Y (DM). Fledged young on Drumbowie Res "lst since war" (NB).

C Pr Cambus Pool from 5 Mar, reared 3Y& present to 4 Sep, also a non breeding Pr in Apr-May (CJH). 2 Prs reared 7Y Gartmorn (MC), 27 on 16 Nov (NB). Prs Craigrie Pond & Delph Pond both had 5Y in Jun (DM).

S Pr Airthrey reared 7Y (MVB), present to 20 Nov (NB).

SWP Blairdrummond: 6 Quarry Loch 15 May, 10 (1Y) on 23 Dec; Pr Daira Loch 10 Apr & 15 May. 1 L.Watston 15 May & 2 from 31 Jul-29 Aug (1Y disappeared) (NB CJH DM). Pr Lake of Menteith reared 1Y (DM). Pr L.Lubnaig reared 1 Y from floating (man-made) site (EAJ). 4 Ad Doune Ponds 22 Aug (CJH). Pr Cromlix 23 Oct & 15 Nov (WRB).

WHOOPER SWAN *Cygnus cygnus (W)*

F 4 ->S Kinneil 20 Feb (CMG). Skinflats:7 on 23 Mar; 6 (3J) on 12 Dec, 14 on 14th (MVB GO RS); 20 (3J) on nearby flood 13 Dec and 22 on 14th (AB). Airth-Letham: 4(1J) 13 Feb to 11 Mar & 8 (1J) on 1-3 Apr; 9 (3J) on 27 Nov (CJH GO DT DMB). 9 Slamannan 23 Oct & 16 Nov (AMcI). 5 Kinneil 27 Nov, 14 on 14 Dec (MVB DT).

C 23 Alva 7 Feb (DMB). 11 Gartmorn 2 Nov & 6 (2J) to Dec (WB MC).

S 25 Gargunnock 5 Apr (CJH D&RJ). 13 Kippen 7 Nov, 66 on 11th, 47 on 16th to 5 on 20th (MT D&RJ). 10 Carron V Res 4 Dec (GO).

SWP 21 Lecropt 23 Jan (DMB). Drip Moss: 23 (2J) on 23 Jan, 58 on 15 Jan, 54 (with 4 Mutes) on 5 Feb & 65 on 12th, 50 on 2 Apr and 45 (last) on 9th. 16 Boquhan 2 Apr to 50 on 9th (DT). 22 Lake of Menteith 5 Feb; 20 L.Dochart 13 Mar (DT), 16 on 14 Dec (NB). 36 L.Lubnaig 31 Mar (DOE), 2 there on 10 Apr expelled to north by Mute Swan (EAJ). 31 L.Doine 4 Apr (EAJ), 1 L.Venachar 10 Apr (CJH). Thornhill 24 on 20 Mar; 4 on 22 Oct & 11(flying over) on 7 Nov, 16 on 14th, 33 on 20 Nov (SS DT). 22 (3J) Drip Moss 20 Nov (DT).

BEWICKS SWAN *Cygnus columbianus (w)*

SWP 2 Drip Moss 26 Mar (MVB).

PINK-FOOTED GOOSE *Anser brachyrhynchus (W)*

The Pinkfeet and Greylag Geese data have been summarised by Dr M V Bell from records of many observers including N Harding, R Johnston, G McShane, M Taylor and K Thompson.

The SNH/RSPB survey of the roosts at the west end of the carse continued in January and February. The lochan on Flanders Moss appeared to be the main Pinkfoot roost, Lake of Menteith being deserted on some dates. The lochan held 1050 birds on 19 January with none at Lake of Menteith, while 2050 flighted into Flanders Moss on 14 February. Frost may then have moved this flock to Lake of Menteith where 2000 flew east at dawn on 16th (KT, NH). There were 974 at Lake of Menteith on 13 March and 400 on 16 April. Up to 1200 flighted from Strathallan to feed at the east end of the carse in January and February with a peak count of 3525 commuting on 12 March (MVB). On 2 April 8050 were found feeding on the carse east of Flanders Moss to the M9 (a record total), of these only 770 roosted in Strathallan (MVB).

Numbers wintering in the upper estuary area have been surprisingly constant at 1000-2500 birds in recent winters and 1994 proved no exception. 1140 were at Kennetpans on 30 January, 1200 at Alloa Inch on 13 and 19 February, 2000 Alloa Inch to Kennetpans on 19 March and 2110 on 2 April. 1300 were still present at Alloa Inch on 30 April and a late bird remained at Cambus on 22 May.

In autumn the first birds were noted flying east at Kippen on 13 September and two days later 30 were at Skinflats and 50 at Upper Glendevon Res. 1800 were along the estuary by 8 October and 2250 at Skinflats on 6 November. Numbers were low in the Forth valley with 805 at Lake of Menteith on 8 October, 1000 Thornhill on 22nd and 750 Flanders Moss on the 28th. By the end of October 2000 were at Loch Mahaick but bad visibility on 12/13 November meant this flock was missed on the National Count. By the third week of November several hundred birds from Carsebreck were regularly feeding in the Forth valley with a maximum of 1270 at Lecropt on 18 December.

BEAN GOOSE *Anser fabalis (W)*

The records suggest a total of 120 birds which often split and move about Ed

F 120 Fannyside 1 Jan, 60 on 11 Feb, 79 on 12th & 60 on 23rd & 24th, last 10 on 9 Mar (BH AMcI GO). 36 L.Ellrig 25 Sep, 110 on 2 & 3 Oct, 81 Fannyside 8 Oct, 100 Slamannan on 4 Oct, 32 on 20th, 53 on 1 Nov & 124 on 16th (DOE AH AMcI GO RS).

S 34 Carron V Res 6 Nov (NB).

WHITE-FRONTED GOOSE *Anser albifrons (w)*

F 2 Slamannan 16 Nov (AMcI).

SWP 2 Blairdrummond Moss 5 Mar (Greenland form) MVB.

GREYLAG GOOSE *Anser anser* (b,W)

In the Forth valley 50 at Lake of Menteith were the only birds located in the Flanders Moss area on 19 January. On 12 February 1370 were feeding with Pinkfeet near Gargunnock and on the 16th at least 580 flighted east out of Loch Rusky, possibly the same birds (KT, NH, MVB). Later field counts in the Forth valley found 815 on 12 March and 680 on 2 April, mostly at the east end of the carse (MVB). Up to 245 were at Gartmorn Dam during February and March with 315 on 5 April and 310 on the 7th (MC). At Cambus there were 147 on 16 January and 300 on 7 April, possibly birds from Gartmorn. 330 feeding at Logie on 19 March probably roosted at Cambus (DMB). The only other flocks of note were 190 Avonbridge on 9 March and 26 at Kinneil on 16 April. 25 -> N L.Lubnaig 10 April (EAJ) probably were on spring migration. There were several summer sightings: 2 Cambus on 22 May, 2 Lake of Menteith on 5 August and 1 Kinneil 14-30 August (2 there from 4 September to December).

In autumn 40 at Carron Valley Res on 16 September were early for Icelandic migrants and much earlier than the next flocks, 20 Loch Ellrig on 2 October (increased to 70 on 18th) and 94 Gartmorn on the 9th. Numbers were low on the carse with 53 Thornhill on 18 October, 190 Loch Rusky and 377 Drip Moss on 13 November (when none at Lake of Menteith). There were 300 feeding near Clackmannan on 18 November (GMcS).

[SNOW GOOSE *Anser caerulescens*]
S 1 (blue phase - usual bird) N.Third Res 18 Oct (WRB).

CANADA GOOSE *Branta canadensis (b)*
SWP 4 Ashfield through March, pr with nest Hutchison Moor 15 May; 20 Cromlix 23 Oct (WRB). Pr with 4Y Blairdrummond 15 May, 11 on 25 Aug, 17 on 23 Dec. 1 L.Watston 15 May, pr with 4Y 30 May to 31 Jul (NB DMB CJH).

BARNACLE GOOSE *Branta leucopsis (w)*
Record passage this October, Ed
F 17 Higgins Neuk 2 Oct & 2 on 27th (DF). Skinflats: 70 (left SW) on 18 Sep, 31 on 29th & 105 on 30th, 914 on 1 Oct, 400 & 200 ->S on 2 Oct , 55 on 10th, 45 on 6 Nov. 2 Fannyside 8 Oct (AB MVB GO DT).
C 150 Kennetpans 8 Oct (DMB).
S 3 Kippen 23 Apr (DMB).
SWP 1 Flanders Moss 14 Apr (BHc). 4 Thornhill 27 Nov (SS). 2 Lecropt 26 Feb. 2 Blairdrummond 5 Mar & 1 on 10th; 2 L.Mahaick 1 Nov. 2 Lecropt 18 Dec (NB MVB). Often with flocks of Pinkfeet.

SHELDUCK *Tadorna tadorna (b,W)*
1403 Forth Estuary 13 Feb & 5162 on 11 Sept (DMB)
F 4750 Kinneil 20 Aug but 6487 on 6 Aug (suggests brief max passage, possibly largest Scottish flock, DMB), 700 on 24 Oct (MVB AMcl). Skinflats: 420 on 12 Jan & 403 on 13 Feb, 216 on 20 Aug, 1200 on 4 Sep & 1160 on 11th, 560 on 6 Nov & 500 on 19th, 390 on 14 Dec (AB DMB MVB); 99 on 1 June & 25 on 12 May (WRB GO). 80 Airth shore 13 Apr (CJH), 73 Higgins Neuk 18 Sep (DF).
C 129 Kennetpans 12 Jan (DMB). 102 Alloa Inch 7 May (DMB). 3 pr Cambus 24 Apr - 13 May, no Y reared (WRB CJH). 75 Tullibody Inch 22 Dec (CJH).
S 1 Carron V Res 10 Mar (DT). 2 over Airthrey 19 Apr (DMB).
SWP 1 Lake of Menteith 5 Feb (DT).

RUDDY SHELDUCK *Tadorna ferruginea*
F 1, possibly 2, Dunmore 8 Oct (DMB). 1 Skinflats 11 Oct (GO). DMB notes size and shape like common Shelduck, buff-brown colour with paler buff heads and black bill and legs, white wing coverts seen when one bird flapped. GO notes that the Skinflats bird survived being shot at three times. DMB's first sighting was of a bird feeding on stubble with Pinkfeet and Barnacle Geese, the second was dabbling on mudflats when the original goose flock was out of sight but had not moved. One or two birds had been seen previously in the Longannet (Fife) area. (In the late summer there was an influx across northwest Europe, presumably of wild origin, and these records may well be related. Thus it seems reasonable to accept the bird(s) as the first record for the area, however it is very difficult to entirely rule out the possibility of an escape Ed. Record still to be validated by BBRC).

WIGEON *Anas penelope (b,W)*

1048 Forth Estuary 12 Jan (DMB).

F Kinneil: Max 495 on 12 Jan, 250 on 6 Feb, 130 on 4 Mar; pair on 6 Jun (AB CJH GO DT); 41 on 29 Oct, 200 on 6 Nov & 356 on 20th, 350 on 3 & 17 Dec (AB GO). Skinflats: 70 on 13 Feb. 3 (1M) on 21 May; M on 12 & 13 Jul, 200 on 2 Oct, 43 on 20 Nov, 500 on 13 Dec but only 65 on 14th (AB MVB AMcI GO DT). 148 Higgins Neuk 23 Jan & 75 on 18 Dec (DF). 40 L.Ellrig 15 Nov (AMcI).

S 97 L.Coulter 28 Nov (NB).

C 2 Cambus 4 & 8 Aug (WRB CJH). 1080 Gartmorn 12 Jan (MC), 64 on 10 Sep & 384 on 21 Oct (NB). 120 Kennetpans 15 Jan (DT), 185 Alloa Inch 6 Nov (MVB).

SWP 62 Forth at Frew Toll 26 Jan (CJH). 2 L.Watston on 9 Jul & 4 on 31st (CJH). 8 Cambusmore 10 Apr, 51 on 3 Oct & 183 on 14 Dec (NB CJH).

*GADWALL *Anas strepera*

C Pr Gartmorn 16 & 21 Oct (NB MC).

TEAL *Anas crecca (B,W)*

632 Forth Estuary 12 Jan (DMB)

F Kinneil; 300 on 6 Feb & 200 on 26th; 10 on 24 Jul, 90 on 17 Sep, 200 on 6 Nov, 130 on 18 Dec (AB HEMD CJH DT). 430 E.Grangemouth 6 Nov & 200 on 29 Dec (MVB CJH). 2 (1st of autumn) Skinflats Ponds 12 Aug, max only 7 on 29th (GO), 184 on estuary 12 Jan & 131 on 14 Dec (MVB).

S 131 Carron V Res 6 Nov (NB).

C 65 Kennetpans 23 Jan (DF), 24 on 11 Sep & 650 on 4 Dec (MVB CJH). 168 Gartmorn on 17 Dec (MC). Cambus max 38 on 5 Apr, only 2 by 20th; 1st of autumn 8 Aug (CJH).

SWP 12 Hutchison dam 4 Apr, 17 on 13 Dec (WRB). F+6Y L.Drunkie 21 Jun, Flanders Moss: F+6Y & F+3Y on 11 Jul (SS).

MALLARD *Anas platyrhynchos (B,W)*

892 Forth Estuary 12 Jan (DMB).

F Skinflats: 348 on 12 Jan, 200 on 23 Jul, 114 on 28 Oct, 291 on 14 Dec (AB MVB GO). Kinneil: 47 on 31 Jul, 85 on 6 Aug, 200 on 18 Sep & 150 on 29th, 200 on 12 Oct (AB DT).

C 74 Kennetpans 23 Jan (DF). 428 Gartmorn 21 Oct (NB).

S 357 Airthrey 17 Jan & 417 on 9 Aug, 379 on 20 Nov (NB MVB). 1st brood 11 Mar, 40 pairs with most early young dying in cold and wet weather, better success later with 27 broods on 30 May (MVB).

SWP 111 Doune Ponds 22 Aug & 101 on 31 Oct (NB CJH). 73 Hutchison Dam 13 Dec (WRB). 23 Blairdrummond in May, 139 on 25 Aug (CJH), 255 on 11 Nov + 265 on Safari Park pond (NB). 12 (7M) L.Watston 15 May, 58 on 31 Jul & 86 on 29 Aug (CJH). 7 L.Venachar 10 Apr, 16 on 25 Aug (CJH).

PINTAIL *Anas acuta (W)*

F Skinflats: 70 on 21 Jan, 69 on 17 Feb, 63 on 6 Mar, 2 on 17 Apr; 1 on 3 Aug, 8 on 9 Sep, 25 on 21 & 25 Oct (only 1M), 20 on 6 Nov & 49 on 20th, 45 on 14 Dec & 65 on 29th (AB MVB DF AMcI GO RS DT); 1 Pintail-Mallard hybrid on 5 Feb (GO). Kinneil : 5 on 29 Oct, 17 on 6 Nov & 6 on 27th (AB RS DT)

C Pr Cambus 15 & 17 Apr (WB CJH), 1 on 4 Aug (WRB).

Area Summary

Jan	Feb	Mar	Apr	-	Aug	Sep	Oct	Nov	Dec
70	69	63	4		2	8	30	49	65

*GARGANEY *Anas querquedula (p)*

F M Skinflats 12 May (WRB GO).

C M Cambus 1 May (WB).

SHOVELER *Anas clypeata (p)*

F M Skinflats 1 May & 26 Jun (AB DMB). 3 Kinneil & F W.Grangemouth 6 Nov (AB MVB).

C M Alloa 30 Apr (DMB). Pr Gartmorn in May, M on 1 Jun (WB MC). M Cambus 8 Apr (WB). 3 Cambus 4 Aug, 5 on 8th & 1 on 30th (WRB CJH).

SWP M L.Watston 15 May (CJH). Pr Hutchison dam 4 Apr & 3 Cromlix 15 Nov (WRB).

POCHARD *Aythya ferina (W)*

C 64 Gartmorn 21 Oct (MC).

S 65 Carron V Res 6 Nov (NB). 8 Airthrey 25 Mar (MVB).

SWP 31 L.Achray & 11 L.Voil 7 Feb (DOE). 46 L.Ard 15 Nov, 30 L.Lubnaig 14 Dec (NB). 1 Blairdrummond 9 Jul, 2 L.Watston 31 Jul & 29 Aug; 1 Doune Ponds 2 Aug (CJH).

TUFTED DUCK *Aythya fuligula (B,W)*

F 2 Skinflats 22 Jul, 1 on 2 Oct (AB). 17 Kinneil 6 Aug (DMB).

S 50 Carron V Res 9 Oct & 4 Dec (NB).

C 107 Gartmorn 16 Jan (MC), 88 on 21 Oct (NB). 1 Cambus 8 Aug (CJH).

S 32 Airthrey 17 Jan & 34 on 13 Dec; at least 4 broods, best for sev years (MVB). 9 (7M) Carron V Res 30 May, 80 by 10 Jul (CJH DT). 10 N.Third Res 18 Oct (WRB).

SWP Flanders Moss: 2 pr + 2M on 12 May & 5 on 11 Jul (SS). 22 Blairdrummond 10 Apr, 90 by 9 Jul (F+7Y), 62 on 25 Aug. 15 Lake of Menteith 16 Apr, 27 on 17 Oct. 37 L.Watston 10 Apr, only 6 on 15 May & F+3Y on 9 Jul, 22 on 31 Jul (CJH NB). 6 (4M) Doune Ponds 26 Mar, Pr Ashfield in Apr (WRB).

*SCAUP *Aythya marila (w)*

9 Forth Estuary 13 Feb (DMB)

F 6 Bo'ness 24 Feb (DOE) - 2 there 2 Mar dabbled in liquid mud 30m from open water (DMB). Kinneil: 1 on 1 & 30 Jan, 20 Feb, 4 on 15 Mar, 1 on 7 & 8 May; 1 on 12 Aug, 2 on 15th & 17 th; 15 on 19 Nov (AB DMB

CMG GO RS). 5 Skinflats 2 Oct & 1 on 14 Dec (AB).
S 1 Carron V Res 6 Nov (NB).

EIDER *Somateria mollissima (w)*
F 21 Blackness 15 Jan & 3 on 23 Feb (CJH DT). 1 Grangemouth 30 Jan, 4(2M) on 8 May, 3 on 12th & only 2M on 28th - possibly breeding nearby (WRB DMB AMcI). 1 Skinflats 12 Jan & 4 on 13 Feb (MVB). M Kinneil 17 May (GO). 2 Kincardine Bridge 12 Mar & 3 on 10 Apr (DF).

GOLDENEYE *Bucephala clangula (W)*
135 Forth Estuary 13 Feb (DMB)
F 14 Dunmore 2 Apr (CJH). 4 Higgins Neuk 6 Nov (DF). 1 Kinneil 13 Aug & 2 on 29 Oct, 19 (est) 19 Nov; 12 Skinflats (est) 13 Feb, 1 (pool) 28 Jan, 5 on 5 Mar & 1 on 2 Oct (AB GO DT).
C 11 Cambus 16 Jan & 5 on 7 Apr (CJH), last 1 on 22 May (WRB). 52 Gartmorn 13 Dec (MC), 1 on 4 Jul (JT).
S Upper Forth: 7 Craigforth 13 Feb, 3 FrewToll on 10 Jan. 5 Kippen Muir 22 Oct (DT). 16 Carron V Res 6 Nov (NB).
SWP 42 Lake of Menteith 16 Apr & 27 on 17 Oct (NB); 3 L.Venachar 10 Apr & 10 on 16th. 1 Blairdrummond GP 10 Apr (CJH). 2 L.Voil & 3 L.Achray 7 Feb (DOE).

*SMEW *Mergus albellus (w)*
F 5 (1F, 4 imm) on estuary Kinneil 19 Nov (AB GO).

RED-BREASTED MERGANSER *Mergus serrator (B,W)*
128 Forth Estuary 13 Feb (DMB).
F 23 Skinflats 13 Feb, 19 on 29 Oct & 41 on 14 Dec (MVB GO). 2M on R.Avon within Grangemouth 30 Jan (DT). 5 Jupiter WG 28 Feb, M to 6 Mar (WRB). 5 Kinneil 29 Sep (AB).
C 1 Cambus 5 & 10 Mar & 2 on 3 Apr, 2 Pr on river 27 Mar (WB CJH).
S 13 Craigforth 26 Feb (MVB). 2 Airthrey 17 Mar (DMB).
SWP Pr Ashfield 5 Mar, F+4Y in late Jul (WRB).

GOOSANDER *Mergus merganser (B,W)*
9 on Forth Estuary 13 Feb (DMB).
F Kinneil: 9 on 3 Oct (GO). Skinflats-Carronmouth: 6 on 12 Jan & 8 Apr, 5 on 15 Feb & 10th; 7 on 11 Sep & 14 Dec,11 on 28 Oct (AB MVB DF GO).
C Cambus (river): 3 on 27 Mar, to 26 on 7 Apr, last 6 on 7 May (WB CJH). 7 Alloa Inch 7 May (DMB). 4 on R.Devon at Dollar 7 Jan (CJH).
S Carron V Res: 7 on 12 Feb, 5 on 10 Mar & 12 (6M) on 4 Dec; Pr 12 Jun (DF JM GO DT). M over Airthrey 25 May (DMB). 3 Stirling 19 Dec (WRB).
SWP Pr Thornhill 12 Feb & L.Voil 27 Mar (DOE), Balvaig on 30 Mar (EAJ). 2 on Forth at Frew 1 Jan. Pr L.Venachar 16 Apr and F on 15 May; F Callander 24 May (CJH). 5 Doune Ponds 9 Apr (WRB). 5 Lecropt 9 May (DMB). Max 5 on Allan Water (Dunblane) Jan-May, 12 (roost)18 Sep, max 13 in Oct & 3 in Nov (BH). Family parties seen Sep/Oct on

L.Dochart, L.Lubnaig, L.Venachar, L.Ard (NB).

*RUDDY DUCK *Oxyura jamaicensis (b)*

C 3M Gartmorn 1 May & 2 on 6th (WB MC).

SWP 2 Pr Flanders Moss 12 May & F on 11 Jul (SS). L.Watston: 4M on 10 Apr, 4(3M) on 30 May, 6 (4M) on 9 Jul & 3 (Pr+M) on 31st. M Doune Ponds 9 Apr & 8 Jul, Pr on 25 May (WRB DMB CJH).

HEN HARRIER *Circus cyaneus (b?, w)*

No definite evidence of nesting; as usual there are no coastal records (Ed).

F M Slamannan 8 Jan (RS).

S F Gargunnock Hills 19 Mar (DT). 1 Carron Valley 11 & 16 Sep (AMcI DT). M Kippen 7 Oct (MT).

SWP Thornhill: 2 on 7 Jan, 2(1M) on 2 Mar, M 16 Aug & 15 Dec (SS). M Blairdrummond Moss 12 Mar (MVB). 2M Flanders Moss 12 Mar, M on 28 Oct , 2 on 22 Dec (DOE). M Lake of Menteith 5 Apr. 1 Blackwater Marshes 19 Dec (NB). M Braes of Doune (Hill House) 4 Apr & mid-Jun, M Hutchison Moor 15 Nov & Ashfield 19 Dec (WRB). M Balfron late Sep (BHc).

SPARROWHAWK *Accipiter nisus (B,W)*

F At Skinflats through year, bred (AB DMB GO).

C Bred Woodhill, Birkhill, Gartmornhill (MC).

S 1 Dunipace 20 Mar, BoA 27 Nov, Stirling 3 Mar & 19 Dec (WRB DOE CJH). At Stirling garden a pair often in April - killed Siskin, on 30th F chased Starling and both killed by hitting a window (D&RJ).

SWP Loch Ard Forest: F chased Raven & Buzzard 30 Jul, Pr feeding 2 juvs 5-15 Aug (CJH). Through year Dunblane, especially May, July (WRB BH); visited garden on 5 occasions Nov-Dec, unsuccessfully chasing finches & tits on feeder (NB).

BUZZARD *Buteo buteo (B,W)*

As breeding bird: widespread SWP, scarce C, overlooked S, no proof F.

F 1->SW (mobbed by crows) Grangemouth 21 Oct (GO).1 Skinflats 12 Sep (RS). 1 Dunipace 20 Mar,1 Denny 24 Feb & 2 on 18 Mar (WRB DOE). 2 Larbert 10 Apr (AMcI). 1 Kinnaird- Letham 26 Feb, 2 Apr, 22 Oct & 2 on 18 Sep (WRB DT). 2 Throsk 2 Apr (DMB). 1 Muiravonside 15 Aug (AMcI).

C Bred Gartmorn, Dollar (MC).

S 5 Carron Valley 12 Feb & 4 on 16 Apr (AMcI GO RS). 2 N.Third Res 9 Jan & 18 Oct (WRB). 2 Touch Res 16 Sep (NB). 2 Plean 28 Feb, 1 ->N Pirnhall 26 Mar (DT). 1 Gargunnock 21 Mar, 1 ->N BoA 3 Sep (CJH).

SWP 8 Lecropt 6 Feb - probably includes birds seen Dunblane-BoA, max 3 on 12 Feb & 6 Airthrey 2 Feb (DMB NB DOE BH DT). 3 Sheriffmuir 22 Oct, 1 at 500m Glentye 17 Aug (WRB). Several prs in breeding season L.Ard Forest, Venachar, Menteith, Pass of Leny, Blairdrummond (CJH BHc AMcI JT) - 4 there on 23 Dec mobbed by crows (NB). On farmland S of Thornhill Jan-Mar, 2 on 26 Jan. 2 Glen Ogle 27 Dec (CJH).

GOLDEN EAGLE *Aquila chrysaetos (b,w)*

SWP Overall: 9 ranges checked, 8 definite pairs and pair probably at the 9th. 4 successful pairs raised 5Y (PSA). 1 traversed L.Ard Forest from L.Chon to Ben Bhreac on 13 Jul (CJH).

OSPREY *Pandion haliaetus (p)*

C 1 Gartmorn 22 Aug (MC).

S 1 ->N Airthrey 14 Apr (MVB), 1 on 17 June (DMB). 1 Carron V Res 3 Jul, 2 on 30th (DMB AKM).

SWP 1st seen Trossachs 1 Apr (AMcI DT).

KESTREL *Falco tinnunculus (B,W)*

F max Skinflats 3 on 12 Jul (GO). Widespread Falkirk-Slamannan (AMcI).

C Pairs reared: 3Y Gartmorn, 2Y Alva Glen, 2Y & 3Y Woodhill (MC).

S Frequent through year (NB); 4 Carron Valley 11 Sep (AMcI).

SWP Generally frequent through year (NB). Scarce L.Ard Forest - 3 August records. 3 over young plantations Glen Ogle 27 Dec (CJH).

*MERLIN *Falco columbarius (b?,w)*

F 1 Falkirk 22 Jan (WRB). 1 Slamannan 24 Feb (AMcI). 1 Carriden 13 Mar (RS). 1 Skinflats 20 Aug, 23 Oct; M there on 30 Sep - chased Skylark which then started full song (AB). 1 Kinneil 12 Oct (DT).

C 1 Kennetpans 2 Apr (DMB).

S 1 Airthrey 11 Feb (DMB). 1 Bridge of Allan 12 Dec (WRB).

SWP 1 Thornhill 2 Mar (CJH). M Blairdrummond 12 Mar (MVB). 1 Flanders Moss 22 Dec (DOE). 1 Ashfield 11 Mar, 25 Oct, 28 Dec (WRB).

PEREGRINE *Falco peregrinus (B,W)*

F Coastal records Jan-May, Sep-Dec (DMB AMcI GO RS DT).

C 2 territories checked, 2 pairs raised 6Y (PSA).

S 6 territories checked: 5 pairs, 1 unoccupied; 3 successful pairs raised 6Y (PSA). Seen around Stirling Feb, Aug-Oct (DMB MB WRB DT).

SWP 21 territories checked: 14 pairs, 2 apparently single birds, 5 unoccupied; 8 successful pairs raised at least 20Y. Breeding success in region slightly less than in 1993, possibly due to a late start with snow in early spring (PSA).1 Flanders Moss on 12 Mar killed Blackheaded Gull (DOE).

RED GROUSE *Lagopus lagopus (B,W)*

Generally under-recorded

F 1 Fannyside Moor 8 Oct (GO). In Nov 1993 recorded in 5 localities, bogs with deep heather, around Darnrig Moss (RSm).

S 8 Lower Earlsburn Res 19 Mar, 4 Kippen Muir 22 Oct (DT), 1 Cringate Muir 28 Nov (NB).

SWP 2 Pr Hill House (Braes Doune) 15 May. 12 in 2 km Sheriffmuir 22 Oct (WRB).

PTARMIGAN *Lagopus mutus (b,w)*

No records received.

*BLACK GROUSE *Tetrao tetrix (B,W)*

There are clearly leks that are not being visited.

C F Ochils 7 May (SH).

S 4(1M) Carron V Forest 10 Mar (DT). 4M Gargunnock Hills (Ballochleam) 13 Feb (WRB).

SWP F Inverlochlarig 10 Feb (DOE). 2M (lek) Ben An 1 May. 8M Callander 5 Jul (DMB). 1Glen Finglass 12 Sep (NB). F Hutchison Moor 22 Dec (WRB).

CAPERCAILLIE *Tetrao urogallus (b,w)*

No records received.

GREY PARTRIDGE *Perdix perdix (B,W)*

F Possibly nested Jupiter WG (WRB). 4 Skinflats 24 Apr, 8(4J) on 10 Oct (AB). 1 Slamannan 7 Mar (AMcl).

C 7 by Devon at Tillicoultry 7 Jan. 12 Cambus 2 Aug (CJH). 18 Gartmorn 2 Nov (WB).

SWP 10 Drip Moss 1 Jan (MVB). 9 Ashfield mid Aug. Pr Kinbuck 22 Oct (WRB).

*RED-LEGGED/CHUKAR PARTRIDGE *Alectoris chukar*

S 1 by Cocksburn Res 8 Jun (CJH).

SWP 1 eating lupins in Dunblane garden 4 Jun - presumed local releases (MVB).

*QUAIL *Coturnix coturnix*

F 1 calling Skinflats 12 & 13 June (GO RS).

SWP 1 calling Blairdrummond 2 Jun (WRB).

PHEASANT *Phasianus colchicus (B,W)*

Though abundant (usually by releases) on fields next to keepered estates Pheasants are often scarce elsewhere - eg only 5 in 76 Km of winter transects on farmland south of Thornhill (CJH).

F Through year at Skinflats, Pr in May & 3M on 10 Oct (AB GO).

SWP Noted at 270m in young spruce on Braes of Doune (WRB).

*WATER RAIL *Rallus aquaticus (w)*

C 1 Gartmorn 4 Jan (WB). 1 Tullibody Inch 11 Oct (CJH).

SWP 1 L.Dhu (Thornhill) 1 May (DT).

MOORHEN *Gallinula chloropus (B,W)*

F 6 Union Canal Brightons 3 Jan (AMcl).

C 1 Tullibody Inch (tidal) 13 Nov (CJH).

S Airthrey: 37 on 17 Jan, 31 on 16 Oct; 12 Prs fledged at least 18 Y from 9 broods & 4 Prs attempted second broods - good breeding season (MVB).

SWP 1 Pr L.Watston Apr-Jul. 4 Doune Ponds 22 Aug (CJH). 2 Pr Ashfield, apparently unsuccessful (WRB).

COOT *Fulica atra (B,W)*

F Max 3 Skinflats 12 Feb to 25 May (GO).

C Max 440 Gartmorn 16 Jan, 300 on 16 Nov; 20 breeding Prs (MC). 4 AoT Cambus 5 Apr, only 3 Aot on 17th & 3Y reared (WRB CJH).

S Airthrey: 53 on 17 Jan & 49 on 5 Sep; 16 Prs with at least 32Y fledged from 10 Prs - broods of 5Y & 7Y- a good year (MVB).

SWP 101 Lake of Menteith 3 Feb, 195 on 19 Dec (NB). 16 Blairdrummond in spring. L.Watston: 9 in Apr, 16 (incl juvs) 31 Jul but only 1 on 29 Aug. 1 L.Venachar 15 May (CJH). 3 Prs Doune Ponds (WRB). 45 Gart Loch Oct-Dec (NB).

OYSTERCATCHER *Haematopus ostralegus (B,W)*

732 Forth Estuary 13 Feb & 576 on 11 Sep (DMB).

F Kinneil: 100 on 30 Jan, 20 on 9 Jul & 110 on 31st (DT); partial albino present from 31Jul to end year (AB). Skinflats: 65 on 12 Jan, 87 on 13 Feb; 47 on 2 Jul, 100 on 22nd & 44 on 26th, 112 on 7 Aug, 37 on 14 Dec (AB MVB).

C 12 by Devon at Tillicoultry 1 Mar (CJH).

S Heard over Stirling early on 1 Feb. 1 Kippen 2 Feb (CJH) & 1 Airthrey on 9th (DMB), 12 Gargunnock 19 Mar (DT). 185 Craigforth 26 Feb, 620 on 5 Mar & 670 on 17th (MVB CJH). 6 AoT Bandeath 7 May (DMB).

SWP 80 Cambusmore 17 Mar & 90 on 10 Apr. 7 Balquhidder on 1 Apr & 7 L.Watston on 10th (CJH EAJ). lst Ashfield 4 Feb, 150 on 13 Mar - now twice as common a breeding bird as Lapwing; last 3 Barbush 20 Aug (WRB).5 ->SW Dunblane 29 May probably first post breeding passage (MVB). 1 found dead at Dunblane 1 Feb had deformed bill (BH).

RINGED PLOVER *Charadrius hiaticula (b,W)*

92 Forth Estuary 13 Feb & 127 on 11 Sep (DMB).

F Skinflats: 13 on 13 Feb, 2 on 24 Mar, 10 on 24 Apr; 11 on 6 to 9 Sep (AB MVB GO). 10 Carronmouth on 28 Aug (JM). Kinneil: lst of autumn 2 on 12 Aug, 11 on 14th, 20 on 29th & 14 on 30th Aug, 2 on 9 Oct (AB DMB DT). Bonnybridge on 21 May: 1 Pr + Pr with 2Y (WRB).

S Pr Lower Earlsburn Res 19 Mar (DT). 2 Carron V Res 3 Jul (DMB).

SWP 1+2Y Barbush 6 Aug (WRB).

GOLDEN PLOVER *Pluvialis apricaria (B,W)*

The small number of likely breeding records may indicate a reduction in range compared with twenty years ago. Passage in March (especially inland) and October (especially by estuary) is well demonstrated (Ed).

310 Forth Estuary 12 Jan & 348 on 11 Sep (DMB).

F 50 Airth 18 Mar (WRB). 50 Blackness 23 Feb & 28 on 7 Aug. 20 Bo'ness (Drum) 27 Nov (CJH). Skinflats: 32 on 12 Jan. lst of autumn 5 on 23 Jul; 65 on 7 Sep & 210 on 22nd, 400 on 2 Oct, 800 on 8th & 536 on 29th; 86 on 14 Dec (AB MVB CJH GO RS DT). 28 Kinneil 4 Dec & 45 on 28th (GO). 14 Higgins Neuk 24 Jul,736 on 2 Oct & 392 on 27th (DF). 350 Grangemouth 16 Oct. 5 Slamannan 1 Jan, 13 Gardrum 4 Oct , 24 L.Ellrig 15 Nov (AMcl).

C 1 Blairdenon 7 May & 12 Jun (SH).
S 300 Gargunnock on 20 Mar (DT).
SWP Thornhill: 33 on 2 Mar, 50 on 9th & 99 on 20th; 18 on 16 Oct & 16 on 28th (DOE CJH SS DT). 40 Blairdrummond Moss 20 Mar & 31 on 4 Apr (DT).14 Drip Moss 27 Nov (CJH). 3 Braes of Doune 23 Nov - very late for hills (WRB).

GREY PLOVER *Pluvialis squatarola (W)*
F 32 Kinneil 13 Mar (GO). Skinflats: 7 on 6 Feb & 8 on 20 Mar; 1st of autumn 1 on 23 Jul to 7 Sep, 9 on 9 Sep, 35 on 2 Oct & 50 on 23rd, 17 on 31 Dec (AB DMB GO DT). 1 Higgins Neuk 2 Oct & 9 on 27th (DF)

LAPWING *Vanellus vanellus (B,W)*
1143 Forth Estuary 12 Jan & 2420 on 11 Sep (DMB).
F Skinflats: 360 on 1 Jan, 243 on 12 Jul, 200 on 7 Aug, 260 on 11 Sep, 100 on 2 Oct & 400 on 12th, 425 on 14 Dec (AB MVB GO DT). Kinneil: 450 on 30 Jan, 410 on 30 Aug, 814 on 1 Sep, 600 on 18th & 250 on 29th (AB CJH DT). 121 Higgins Neuk 23 Jan, 270 on 18 Sep & 845 on 6 Nov (DF). 24 Slamannan 1 Jan & 200 on 11 Sep. 15 L.Ellrig 3 Mar, 60 on 2 Oct (AMcI).
S Display at Kippen 6 Mar, 100 Cambusbarron 5 Mar. 200 Pirnhall 19 Aug (DT). 15 AoT Bandeath 7 May (DMB).
C Tullibody Inch: 190 on 14 Aug, 500 on 11 Oct & 700 on 13 Nov, 1100 on 4 Dec (MVB CJH). 4 AoT Cambus 20 Apr, 2 on nests there + 1AoT on 7 May (CJH).
SWP Thornhill: 9 on 1 Jan, absent mid Jan to late Feb, 140 on 2 Mar (CJH). 90 Ashfield 30 Mar, 30 prs Ashfield-Kinbuck but only 2Y seen due to ploughing etc; 63 on 14 Dec were late (WRB). Pr bred Keir roundabout, 3 Pr + 4Y Lecropt 4 Jun but 3 nests destroyed (WRB). 600 Lecropt 20 Aug (MVB).

KNOT *Calidris canutus (W)*
4612 Forth Estuary 12 Jan (DMB).
F Kinneil: 2000 on 4 Jan, 4430 on 12th & 1000 on 30th, 1500 on 6 Feb, 850 on 27 Mar 7, 100 on 17 Apr & 134 on 23rd; lst of autumn 2 Ad on 9 Jul, 9 on 31st, 300 on 6 Nov & 1000 on 27th, 2000 on 3 Dec & 3000 on 18th (AB CJH GO DT). Skinflats: 180 on 12 Jan & 400 on 30th, 800 on 13 Feb, last 3 on 14 May; lst of autumn 8 on 25 Jun, few in Jul & Aug, 10 on 7 Sep,1300 on 14 Dec (MVB AMcI GO). 60 Higgins Neuk 27 Oct & 4 on 6 Nov (DF).

*SANDERLING *Calidris alba (p)*
F 1 Skinflats 8 May & 1 on 22 Jul (AB GO). 3 Kinneil 31 Jul (AB).

*LITTLE STINT *Calidris minuta (p)*
F Skinflats: 1 on 5 & 9 Sep (AB RS).

CURLEW SANDPIPER *Calidris ferruginea (p)*
F 1 Carronmouth 23 Aug (JM). Kinneil: 1 on 4 Sep, 2 on 8th & 18th, 5 on 17th (DMB RS DT). Skinflats:3 on 7 & 8 Sep, 6 on 9th & 1 on 11th, 3 on

6 Oct & 2 on 7th (AB MVB GO RS).
Area Summary (half monthly)

Aug	Sep	Oct
0 1	8 5	3 0

DUNLIN *Calidris alpina* (b?,W)
6356 Forth Estuary 13 Feb & 1099 on 11 Sep (DMB).
F Kinneil: 2000 on 12 Jan & 1500 on 30th; 25 on 31 Jul, 500 on 24 Oct (CJH AMcI DT). Skinflats: 2170 on 12 Jan, 2430 on 13 Feb, 150 on 24 Apr & 158 on 7 May; 100 on 22 Jul, 300 on 3 Aug, 780 on 11 Sep, 575 on 7 Oct & 300 on 19th, 700 on 6 Nov, 1450 on 14 Dec (AB MVB DOE GO). Higgins Neuk: 7 on 24 Jul, 290 on 2 Oct, 350 on 6 Nov (DF).
S 7 Carron V Res 3 Jul (DMB) - presumably early migrants (Ed).

RUFF *Philomachus pugnax (p)*
F Skinflats: 3 on 25 Aug, 4 on 6 Sep & 6 on 11th, 2 on 20th & 23rd; 9 on 2 & 3 Oct, 4 on 10th, 3 on 11th & 28th (AB MVB GO DT RS). Kinneil: 2 on 8 Sep,10 on 16th to 18th, 2 on 3 Oct (DMB HEMD RS DT). Higgins Neuk: 1 on 22 Aug & 3 on 2 Oct (DF).
C 1 Cambus 8 & 11 Aug (WB CJH).
Area Summary (half monthly)

Aug	Sep	Oct
1 4	8 12	14 5

*JACK SNIPE *Lymnocryptes minimus (w)*
F Kinneil: 2 on 4 Jan & 6 on 9th, 3 on 26 Feb, 1 on 27 Mar; 4 on 3 Oct & 3 on 30th, 1 on 27 Nov (GO RS DT). 1 E.Grangemouth 6 Nov (MVB).

SNIPE *Gallinago gallinago (B,W)*
Probably under-recorded in breeding season but may have decreased (Ed).
33 Forth Estuary 12 Jan (DMB).
F Kinneil: Max in Jan 25 on 9th; 6 on 31 Jul, 13 on 13 Aug, 22 on 3 Oct & 27 on 29th,30 on 27 Nov (GO RS DT). 33 E.Grangemouth 12 Jan & 35 on 6 Nov (MVB). 19 Higgins Neuk 18 Dec (DF).
C 1 Blairdenon 7 May (SH). 3 Cambus 31 Jul (WB). (Remarkably scarce here this autumn Ed)
SWP 5 Ashfield 5 Aug, 4 on 21 Dec (WRB).

WOODCOCK *Scolopax rusticola (B,W)*
Under-recorded in breeding season (Ed).
C Bred Cowpark (Gartmorn), Dollar Glen (MC).
F 1 Brightons 1 Jan (AMcI). 1 Grangemouth 28 Nov flew into school window and broke neck, weight 297.5 gm (JW).
SWP 1 Thornhill 11 Mar (SS).

BLACK-TAILED GODWIT *Limosa limosa (W)*
F Moderate numbers were at Kinneil from January to late April with Skinflats only being used in April - the apparent rise in the area total in late April is probably double counting of the same flock. Few birds were present in summer until late July, Kinneil was the main site with

a maximum of 69 on 4 Sep and moderate numbers to the end of the year; there were few at Skinflats after mid September (AB DMB HEMD DOE GO RS DT). 9 Higgins Neuk 7 Aug (DF).

C 1 Cambus 21 May. 6 Tullibody Inch 7 Aug (DMB).

	Jan	Feb	Mar	Apr	May	Jun	Jul	Aug	Sep	Oct	Nov	Dec
Knnl	12 17	4 5	12 25	3 20	2 1	0 0	0 56	59 50	69 43	46 50	60 52	34 21
Sknf	0 0	0 0	0 3	10 26	1 1	0 4	5 18	16 5	16 3	1 0	0 0	0 0
Area	12 17	4 5	12 28	13 46	3 3	0 4	5 74	90 55	85 46	47 50	60 52	34 21

BAR-TAILED GODWIT *Limosa lapponica (W)*

208 Forth Estuary 12 Jan (DMB).

F 120 Kinneil 4 Jan & 203 on 12th, 100 on 30th (CJH DT); 17 on 24 Oct, 200 on 11 Dec (AMcI DT). Skinflats: 3 on 7 May, 2 in SP 7 Jul then a few until 7 Oct with max of 5 on 7 & 20 Sep (AB GO). 1 Higgins Neuk 7 Aug, 18 Sep, 18 Dec (DF).

WHIMBREL *Numenius phaeopus (p)*

F Skinflats: 2 on 3 May, 4 on 13th, last 1on 27th. 1st of autumn 8 Jul, 2 on 9th & 7 on 26th, 6 on 6 Aug and last on 11th (AB DMB WRB GO RS). Kinneil: 1st on 9 Jul & 3 on 31st, 1 on 6 & 12 Aug & 1 on 4 & 5 Sep (AB GO RS DT). 1 Kincardine Bridge 8 May (DMB). 1 Higgins Neuk 26 Jun & 2 on 24 Jul (DF).

C 2 Cambus 21 May (DMB).

S 1 over M9 Stirling 2 May (AH).

SWP 1 -> E Balquhidder 12 May (EAJ).

Area Summary (half monthly)

May	Jun	Jul	Aug	Sep
6 2	0 1	3 12	7 0	1 0

CURLEW *Numenius arquata (B,W)*

The March return & passage is clear in inland records but only apparent in the inner estuary data (Ed).

1137 Forth Estuary 13 Feb & 1081 on 11 Sept (DMB).

F 70 Bo'ness (Drum) 6 Jan (CJH). 30 by M9 Grangemouth in mid Jan (WRB). Kinneil: 200 on 30 Jan, 200 on 9 Jul, 400 on 4 Sep; a very pale leucistic bird on 6 Aug (DMB DT). Skinflats: 100 on 7 Jan, 308 on 13 Feb, 136 on 29 Mar, 110 on 12 Apr; 11 on 27 Jun, 81 on 12 Jul, 60 on 6 Aug, 313 on 11 Sep, 137 on 6 Nov, 55 on 19 Nov, 131 on 14 Dec (AB MVB GO). Higgins Neuk; 251 on 12 Mar, 103 on 10 Jul, 466 on 7 Aug (DF). 40 Airth shore 13 Apr (CJH). 20 Slamannan 10 Mar (AMcI).

C 30 Cambus 30 Jan, 56 on 5 Mar & 300 on 10th. 50 Tullibody Inch 11 Oct (WB CJH). 60 by Devon at Tillicoultry 19 Mar (CJH).

SWP Return to Ashfield 3 Mar. 11 Balquhidder 1 Apr (EAJ). 120 Drip Moss & 55 nr Gargunnock on 12 Mar (MVB). 9 AoT Braes of Doune (Bows-Hill House)(WRB). 1 dead by M9 Keir 20 Jun (NB).

SPOTTED REDSHANK *Tringa erythropus (p)*

F 1 Kinneil 13 Aug & 2 on 17 Sep (DMB DT). Skinflats: 1 from 12 Feb to 6 May, moulted from winter to summer plumage (AB AMcI GO RS DT). 1st of autumn 2 on 25 Aug & 1 to 9 Sep, 1 on 23 Sep & 2 on 6 Oct, last on 19th (AB WRB GO RS).

C 1 Cambus 4 Sep (CJH).

REDSHANK *Tringa totanus (B,W)*

2373 Forth Estuary 13 Feb & 2710 on 11 Sept (DMB)

F 50 Bo'ness 24 Feb (DOE). Kinneil: 700 on 12 Jan, 300 on 17 Apr; 270 on 31 Jul, 700 on 6 Aug & 920 on 14th, 1030 on 4 Sep, 500 on 24 Oct (DMB CJH AMcl DT). Skinflats: 1170 on 12 Jan, 1240 on 13 Feb, 83 on 12 Apr, 40 on 12 May; Bred here, 2Y seen July; 50 on 9 Jul & 400 on 22nd, 400 on 7 Aug, 835 on 11 Sep, 520 on 7 Oct, 1060 on 11 Nov, 960 on 14 Dec (AB WRB MVB). Higgins Neuk: 120 on 26 Feb, 197 on 12 Mar; 78 on 7 Aug, 157 on 22nd (DF).

C 1 AoT Cambus 7 to 27 May (WRB CJH).

SWP 2 AoT Kinbuck 14 Apr (WRB).

GREENSHANK *Tringa nebularia (p)*

F Skinflats: 1 on 27 Apr, 1 on 3 May & from 16 to 22 May, 1 on 26 Jun, 2 on 22 Jul, 3 on 3 Aug & 1 from 11 to 15 Aug,1 on 6 Sep, 2 on 7th, 1 from 23 Sep to 10 Oct & 2 on 8 Oct (AB DMB DOE CJH GO RS). 1 Carronmouth 23 Aug (JM). Kinneil: 1st on 30 Aug, 3 on 4 Sep, 2 on 5th & last on 12 Oct (AB DMB RS DT). 1 Higgins Neuk on 18 Sep (DF).

C 1 Cambus 13 & 19 Apr (WB). 1 Tullibody Inch 7 Aug (DMB).

SWP 1 Barbush GP 6 & 10 Aug (WRB).

Area Summary (half monthly)

Apr	May	Jun	Jul	Aug	Sep	Oct
1 2	1 1	0 1	0 2	4 2	5 2	2 0

*GREEN SANDPIPER *Tringa ochropus (p)*

F 2 Skinflats 12 May (WRB). 1 Kinneil 30 Jul, 2 on 30th Aug & 1 on 5 Sep (RS DT). 1 Higgins Neuk 18 Dec (DF- winter records very unusual in this area, Ed).

C 1 Cambus 4 Aug (WRB).

SWP 1 Barbush 24 Apr, 5 & 6 Aug (WRB).

Area Summary (half monthly)

Apr	May	Jul	Aug	Sep	Dec
0 1	2 0	0 1	2 2	1 0	0 1

COMMON SANDPIPER *Tringa hypoleucos (B)*

F Kinneil: 1st of autumn 1 on 9 Jul, 10 on 30 Jul, 17 on 3 Aug, 9 on 6th, 3 on 12th & 30th, last 1 on 18 Sept (AB DMB GO DT). 2 Carronmouth 23 Aug (JM). Skinflats: 1st on 13 Jul, 1 on 23rd (GO). Higgins Neuk: 3 on 10 Jul, 1 on 7 Aug & 18 Sep (DF).

C lst Gartmorn 22 Apr (MC). 2 Cambus 19 Jul (CJH).

SWP 2 Balquhidder 3 Apr (EAJ) -early date, Ed. 4 Dunblane 27 Apr (BH). 1 Lake of Menteith 29 Apr (DT).6 Barbush 23 Apr, 3 on 6 Aug (bred in GP), last 2 on 17th (WRB). In summer at Blairdrummond GP & Teith at Callander (CJH).

Area autumn totals, estuary :

Jul	Aug	Sep
5 13	18 5	1 2

TURNSTONE *Arenaria interpres (W)*
61 Forth estuary 13 Feb (DMB).
F 12 Blackness 23 Feb (CJH). 2 Skinflats 23 Jul & 1 Kinneil 15 Jan, 2 on 6 Aug, 1 on 20 Nov (GO DT)

*POMARINE SKUA *Stercorarius pomarinus (p)*
F Skinflats Ponds 2 Oct: 4 Ad + 1 juv flew off high WSW (GO). Later, 5 Ad + 1 Juv, circled high but returned to estuary (AB) . 3 (1 pale Ad) Kinneil 12 Oct, flew off W, climbing over docks (DT).

*ARCTIC SKUA *Stercorarius parasiticus (p)*
F 1 Skinflats 3 Aug, 2 on 2 Oct (chasing Sandwich terns), 1(pale phase) 19 Oct (AB DOE RS DT).

*LONG-TAILED SKUA *Stercorarius longicaudus*
F At least 3, probably 10, off Kinneil 13 Aug (DT). At 16.55 7 pale phase skuas were seen flying W low over the river channel, not coming closer than c 2000 m; these features were noted, using a x30 telescope (with some heat shimmer): plumage very contrasted with dark caps, very clean and pale throat and breast with darker ventral area, wings were narrow, lacking primary flashes and appearing a rather pale grey-brown when caught by the sun; the birds climbed steeply when close to the docks and circled high up, appearing very slim and flexible with attenuated rear and tail though tail streamers could not be seen for certain. At 17.25 3 more skuas were seen flying west but higher and nearer so that their long and flexible tail streamers could be noted clearly. *(Summary of longer note, although in some recent autumns many have been seen flying west near the Forth bridges this is our first record since 1934, Ed).*

*GREAT SKUA *Stercorarius skua (p)*
F 4 Skinflats 19 Oct, left W (GO).

*LITTLE GULL *Larus minutus (p)*
F Skinflats: 1 (2nd summer) on 12 May, 1 (lst summer) on 22 May & 25 Jun, 1 Ad on 9 Jul (AB GO).

BLACK-HEADED GULL *Larus ridibundus (B,W)*
F 2400 Airth 26 Nov (CJH). Higgins Neuk: 550 on 23 Jan, 195 on 10 Jul (DF). Skinflats Ponds:150 on 7 Jul, 450 on 29 Sep, 300 on 22 Oct (AB).
C Parties hawking on 3 Sep: 400 Kennetpans, 100 Airthrey (S) & 100 BoA (S) (CJH).
SWP At Ashfield 150 by 27 Mar, good season with at least 120 pairs rearing 150Y (WRB).

COMMON GULL *Larus canus (B,W)*
SWP Few Thornhill Jan-Feb but 500 on 2 Mar (CJH). 18 Blairdrummond Quarry Pond 10 Apr. 6 nests (+6 imms) L.Watston 15 May, 1 nest L.Rusky 24 May (CJH). 8 AoT Barbush, no nests found; 250 Kinbuck 14 Dec (WRB).

LESSER BLACK-BACKED GULL *Larus fuscus (b,S)*

F 1 Grangemouth 20 Jan (WR). 4 Carronmouth 5 Feb (GO) & 2 Kinneil on 6th (AB). 3 Skinflats 11 Mar, 39 on 13th (GO). 1 Shieldhill 7 Mar, 4 Avonbridge 2 Apr (AMcI). Grangemouth: 11 AoT Zeneca colony + 2 nests on sawmill, at least 2 broods seen (WRB HEMD). 36 (30 juv) Skinflats on 29 Jul & 59 (47 juv) on 31st (AB). 65 Kinneil 24 Jul (CJH).

C 30 around Cambus bond roofs 4 Aug (WRB).

S 1 Stirling 7-28 Jan, 9 Dec (DT). 1 Airthrey 26 Jan (DMB). 1 BoA 30 Nov (WRB).

HERRING GULL *Larus argentatus (b?,S,W)*

F 2300 Kinneil 29 Dec (CJH). 1AoT Zeneca, breeding not confirmed (WRB).

S 2300 Fallin tip 5 Mar (CJH).

*ICELAND GULL *Larus glaucoides*

F 1 Kinneil 15 Aug - plumage very worn, probably lst summer (AB).

GREAT BLACK-BACKED GULL *Larus marinus (S,W)*

Highly under-reported (Ed).

SWP 4 (3 Ad) at stranded salmon Kinbuck 13-17 Dec (WRB).

*KITTIWAKE *Rissa tridactyla (P,w)*

F 20 on Forth at Skinflats 12 May (GO). 1 Blackness 1 Apr (CJH). 1 Higgins Neuk (roosting) 24 Jul (DF).

S 1 lst Winter (fresh predator kill) Carron Bridge 14 Feb (AF).

SANDWICH TERN *Sterna sandvicensis (P)*

F 230 Blackness 7 Aug (CJH).15 Kinneil 6 Aug (DT), 2 on 29 Sep, 4 on 9 Oct were late (AB). Skinflats: 3 on 12 May & 9 on 25 Jun (GO); 3 high to W on 1 Sep, 20 on 2 Oct - some harried by Arctic Skua (AB DT). Higgins Neuk: 16 on 7 Aug, 43 on 2 Oct (DF).

C 2 Alloa Inch 7 May (DMB). 120 Kennetpans 3 Sep (CJH).

COMMON TERN *Sterna hirundo (B)*

F Skinflats: 1st on 1 May (AB), 25 on 3 & 12 May (AB WRB GO DT). At the Grangemouth colony 107, 30 sitting, on 8 May; at least 89 pairs nested rearing 51Y, a max of 124 Ad present on 6 Aug when 15+ nests were still active (DMB). Higgins Neuk: 20 on 10 Jul & 36 on 7 Aug (DF). 2 Kinneil 9 Oct (AB).

C 1 Alloa 30 Apr (DMB)

S 2 feeding 2 fledged young Carron V Res 30 Jul (AKM).

*ARCTIC TERN *Sterna parasidaea*

F 2 Skinflats 23 Jul, left W (GO). *(lst record for many years, Ed).*

GUILLEMOT *Uria aalge (W)*

F 1 Skinflats Ponds 17 Feb (RS) & 5 at Kincardine Bridge (CJH). 37 (35 dead) Blackness 23 Feb, 1 survivor chased by Great Blackbacked Gull (CJH). 6 dead Kinneil 26 Feb (DT). 224 dead 26/27 Feb R.Carron-

Kincardine Bridge (DM). 2, +1 dead, Airth Shore 19 Feb & 43 dead on 13 Apr (CJH). 6 Higgins Neuk 26 Feb & 1 on 12 Mar (DF). *(Most records refer to the large wreck in February, Ed).*

S 1 Causewayhead 14 Feb, on road and then mobbed by Rooks (NB). 1 dead on road Airthrey 23 Feb (MVB).

*RAZORBILL *Alca torda (w)*

F 4 dead Skinflats 26/27 Feb (DM).

ROCK DOVE / FERAL PIGEON *Columba livia (B,W)*

SWP 100 Dunblane through year (BH).

STOCK DOVE *Columba oenas (B,W)*

F 5 Skinflats 17 May (GO).

S 15 Bandeath 7 May (DMB).

SWP Max 10 on 9.5km transect Thornhill Jan-Mar (CJH). 4 Blairdrummond 15 May (CJH).2 Barbush 14 Oct (WRB).

WOODPIGEON *Columba palumba (B,W)*

S 460 Cambuskenneth 5 Jan. 100 BoA 9 Oct (CJH).

SWP 2000 Hill of Row 26 Feb (MVB). Max 41 on 9.5km transect Thornhill Jan-Mar. 82 on seeded field Blairdrummond 1 May (CJH).

COLLARED DOVE *Streptopelia decaocto (B,W)*

Under-reported, but scarce away from suburbs and large farms (Ed)

S 10 BoA 30 Nov (WRB).

SWP Max 4 Dunblane in Apr (BH).

CUCKOO *Cuculus canorus (B)*

F 1 Skinflats 8 May (GO).

C 1 Dollar Glen 25 May (SH).

SWP 1 L.Dhu (Thornhill) 1 May (DT). 2 Glen Lochay 6 May. 1 Braes Doune 15 May (WRB). 2 L.Ard Forest 26 May (CJH). 2 Lake of Menteith 31 May (BHc). Juv Sheriffmuir 17 Aug (WRB).

*BARN OWL *Tyto alba (b,w)*

F 1 E of Boness 26 Dec (RS).

S 1 Craigforth 6 Mar (WR).

SWP 1 over A9 at Dunblane 20 Mar & 2 Apr (MVB), 1 dead by Doune road flyover 17 Jun (NB).

TAWNY OWL *Strix aluco (B,W)*

C 2 Brothie Burn Woods 2 Jan (WB). 1 Dollar 22 May, 1 Dollarbeg 13 Jun (SH).

S 1 dead on road Carron V Res 30 May; 2 nestboxes on 20 Feb already had 1 egg each, 3Y in nest box there (AF BHc). 2 Stirling 10 Oct (DT).

SWP 1 Arnprior 8 Mar (DT). 1 dead on M9 at Keir 23 Jun (NB). Dunblane Nov-Dec (WRB). 1 fell down chimney Thornhill 7 Dec, released unhurt (SS) - (chose an RSPB worker, Ed).

*LONG-EARED OWL *Asio otus (b,w)*

F Ad + calling young at nest found Skinflats 28 May, 2Y (1 fledged) on 2 Jun (DMB MVB).

SHORT-EARED OWL *Asio flammeus (b,W)*

F Kinneil: Max 2 early Jan, then 1 to 25th; 2 on 4 Sep then 1 to 9 Oct (DMB CMG RS DT). Skinflats: 1 on 21 Jan & 13 Mar to 21 Apr; 1 on 3 Aug to 11 Oct (AB DOE DF GO RS DT). On 1 Oct 1 flew in from Fife over Forth, mobbed by Crows (AB).

S 3 AoT Touch Muir 24 May (CJH).1 Carron V Res 3 Jul (DMB).

SWP 4 Glen Ogle 27 Dec in young plantation (CJH).1 Flanders Moss 22 Dec (P.Martin).

Estuary half month summary

Jan	Feb	Mar	Apr	Aug	Sep	Oct	Nov	Dec
3 2	2 1	2 2	1 1	1 1	3 2	1 0	0 0	0 0

NIGHTJAR *Caprimulgus europaeus (?b)*

SWP None found Queen Elizabeth Forest Park this summer (per Forest Enterprise).

SWIFT *Apus apus (B)*

F 1 Skinflats 12 & 13 May, 1 Falkirk on 13th (AB GO DT). 25 Higgins Neuk 24 Jul (DF), 17 Blackness 8 Aug (CJH).

C 50 Cambus 2 Aug (CJH). 11 L.Ard Forest 30 Jul, last 2 on 15 Aug (CJH).

S 3 Stirling 9 May, last on14 Aug (DT). BoA: 4 on 7 May, 55 on 20 Jul & 120 on 31st (DMB CJH).

SWP 1 Strathyre 9 May (D&RJ). 3 Dunblane 14 May, max 11in Jul, last 24 Aug (BH). On 15 May: 1 Doune, 2 Balquhidder, 2 Glen Buckie (DT).

KINGFISHER *Alcedo atthis (b,w)*

C 1 Pr Devon (Dollar) (MC).

S 1 Carronbridge 20 Jan (AF).

GREEN WOODPECKER *Picus viridis (B,W)*

C 1Tillicoultry 19 Mar (CJH). 2 Pr Woodhill, 1 Pr Alva Glen & Tillicoultry (MC).

S 1 Carron V Res 12 Feb (DF). 1 Witches Craig 1 Apr, Mine Wood 9 Apr, Sauchie Crags 18 Oct (WRB). 2 calling SE of Gargunnock 20 Apr (JM).

SWP 3 sites L.Ard Forest 21 Mar - 12 Apr (CJH). 1 Doune Ponds 9 Apr (WRB).

GREAT SPOTTED WOODPECKER *Dendrocopus major (B,W)*

Greatly under reported from S & SWP

F 1 Bo'ness 12 Feb (RS). 1 Jupiter WG 25 Jun (WRB).

S 1 Kippen 24 Nov (D&RJ).

SWP 1 Thornhill 10 Jan (CJH). 1 Port of Menteith 10 Apr (AMcI). Callander 2 Jul (JT). 1 Dunblane 31 Oct (WRB).

SKYLARK *Alauda arvensis (B,W)*

F Skinflats: 25 on 5 Jan & 13 Feb, 40 on 14 Dec. Song at Kinneil 6 Feb (AB).

C 22 Dollar 1 Mar, ->N very high and singing (presumably return to Ochils CJH).

S 60 Gargunnock 20 Mar (DT). 200 Gogar (rape stubble) 30 Jan & 34 on 9 Oct. 9 ->SW BoA 9 Oct (CJH).

SWP 200 Ashfield 3 Mar, song from 9 Feb (WRB). Thornhill, song from 2 Feb, 100 on 2 Mar, 40 on 20th (CJH DT). 400 Lecropt 26 Feb (MVB). 120 Drip Moss (stubble) 27 Nov (CJH).

SAND MARTIN *Riparia riparia (B)*

F lst Carronshore 17 Apr, 100 Larbert Pond on 26th (AB). 2 Skinflats 23 Apr, last 1 on 20 Sep (GO). 10 Kinneil 31 Jul, 40 on 30 Aug (DT).

C 1 Gartmorn 27 Mar (MC), 10 on 2 Apr (CJH).

S 1 Airthrey 28 Mar, 8 on 1 Apr, 9 on 4th & 150 on 22nd (DMB MVB).

SWP 10 Lake of Menteith 1 Apr (DT). 2 Dunblane 12 Apr, flocks from 21st; still around nest sites 21 Aug (BH). 5 Barbush GP 13 Apr, 300 nestholes. 150 (mainly juvs) Ashfield 21 Aug (WRB). Small colony Inverlochlarig 1 Jun (DOE).

SWALLOW *Hirundo rustica (B)*

First birds widespread around 10 April, major arrival from 22nd.

F lst Carronshore 10 Apr, 15 on 23rd (AB). lst Skinflats 22 Apr, 7 on 23rd; 12 on 20 Sep, last 4 on 2 Oct (AB GO DT).

C 1st Gartmorn 22 Apr (MC). 60 Cambus 4 Sep, 16->S Kennetpans 11 Sep (CJH).

S 2 Airthrey 22 Apr (MVB DMB). 1 BoA 25 Apr (DT)

SWP 1st Ashfield 12 Apr, 3 Prs nested (WRB). lst Dunblane 18 Apr, not seen after 8 Aug (BH). 1st Thornhill 23 Apr (SS).

HOUSE MARTIN *Delichon urbica (B)*

F lst Carronshore 25 Apr (AB).Still feeding young in nest at Bo'ness 22 Sep (RS).

S 1 Airthrey 23 Apr (MVB). 1 BoA 25 Apr, at nest 9 Oct (DMB). 1 BoA 1 Oct (DT).

SWP 2 Ashfield 23 Apr, 6 nests (WRB). Colony Kilbryde Castle 5 Jun. 30 Dunblane 7 & 15 Sep (BH).

TREE PIPIT *Anthus trivialis (B)*

C 6 AoT Woodhill (MC).

S Frequent at Carron V Res (mouth of Carron) 30 May (CJH).

SWP 1 L.Dhu (Thornhill) 1 May (DT). 5 AoT Glen Ample 30 Apr & 2 Ben An on 1 May (WRB). Singing Glen Lochay 6 May. 1 AoT Dounans 19 May (HEMD).

MEADOW PIPIT *Anthus pratensis (B,W)*

F 30 Skinflats 2 Apr (AB).

C 12 Kennetpans 11Sep (CJH).

SWP 33 Thornhill 10 Jan 7 & 18 on 2 Feb (CJH). Small flocks ->N Strathyre 25 Mar (EAJ), abundant Monachyle Glen on 30th (DJP). 50 ->N Dunblane 8 Apr; on 9th big flocks on carse - 350 Lecropt, 150 +60

+100 +120 Blairdrummond Moss (MVB); 160 in stubble L.Watston 10 Apr (CJH) (snow at 500m - these flocks presumably birds driven from hills or held up). 16 late migrants on Blairdrummond carse 1 May (CJH). Late hill birds: 8 at 300m Sheriffmuir 22 Oct, 2 Braes Doune 23 Nov (WRB).

ROCK PIPIT *Anthus petrosus (w)*
No records received

WATER PIPIT *Anthus spinoletta*
F DT points out a record for Kinneil, 13 Nov 1977, in Scottish Birds (1978) Vol 10, p148. This can now be added to the area list as a full species.

*YELLOW WAGTAIL *Motacilla flava*
F F Skinflats 3 May, with Pied Wagtails round cattle trough (AB).

GREY WAGTAIL *Motacilla cinerea (B,w)*
F 1 occasionally at Jupiter WG from 26 Mar (WRB). 1 Higgins Neuk 18 Dec (DF).
C 1 wintered on Devon at Tillicoultry Jan-Mar (CJH). 1 Cambus 10 Mar (WB). 2 AoT in 5 km at Crook of Devon (MM).
S 1st of autumn at Stirling 11 Aug (DT). 1 BoA late Dec (WRB).
SWP Return to Thornhill 2 Mar (CJH). At Dunblane Mar-Oct, with juvs 12 Jun (BH). Good breeding year in Trossachs (HR). 2 Aot Inverlochlarig 1 Jun (DOE). Callander 2 Jul, Pass of Leny 5 Jul (JT). 2 L.Katrine 12 Sep (NB).1 at Barbush to end year (WRB). 1 Blairdrummond 23 Dec (NB).

PIED WAGTAIL *Motacilla alba (B,W)*
F Skinflats: 28 on 2 Apr. White Wagtails *M.a.alba* - 1 on 3, 12 & 17 Apr, 2 on 23rd-24th; 1 (with 30 Pieds) Kinneil on 15 Aug (AB GO).
C 2 on 8.5km transect Thornhill Jan-early Mar, 8 on 19 Mar (CJH).
S 110 at Airthrey roost 29 Nov (CJH).
SWP 30 Lecropt 7 Feb (BH). 1 on 9.5km transect Thornhill Jan-early Mar, 7 on 20 Mar (CJH). 15 Dunblane in Oct, 2 chased Sparrowhawk on 28 Jul (WRB BH).

DIPPER *Cinclus cinclus (B,W)*
C 5 AoT in 5 km at Crook of Devon (MM).
SWP A fair breeding season (HR). Nested under railway bridges at Barbush & Dunblane (WRB), juv seen in Jun (BH). Ad+new fledged juv on Teith at Callendar 24 May (CJH). In autumn at L.Katrine, Arklet, Doine, Voil, Finglas, Culnagreine (NB).

WREN *Troglodytes troglodytes (B,W)*
Under-recorded (Ed).
SWP No change on Blairdrummond spring transect (CJH).

HEDGE SPARROW *Accentor modularis (B,W)*
Under-recorded (Ed).
S Singing Stirling 12 Nov (WRB).

SWP 1 record on 4 km spring transect at Blairdrummond, compare 10 for Robin (CJH). 4 Dunblane 26 Jan, 2-3 for rest year (BH).

ROBIN *Erithacus rubecula (B,W)*
No significant records

REDSTART *Phoenicurus phoenicurus (B)*
F 1 Wallacebank Wood 15 May, 2 on 22nd (AMcl).
C 1 Pr Woodhill (MC).
SWP 33 Prs at Trossachs colony reared 174 Y (HR). M Strathyre 27 Apr (EAJ), 3 AoT Glen Ample 30 Apr (WRB). Singing Glen Lochay 6 May. 10 Rhuveag (Balquhidder) 8 May (DT).

WHINCHAT *Saxicola rubetra (B)*
Under-recorded as breeding (Ed).
F 2 Skinflats 2 May; 5 (4Juv) on 17 & 23 Jul, 7 on 2 Aug, 3 on 2 Sep, last on 11 Sep - prob roosted in reeds (AB GO).1 Kinneil 12 Aug (DT).
C 1 Tullibody Inch 14 Aug (CJH).
S A few Carron V Res (Carronmouth) 30 May. 3 AoT Cocksburn Res 8 Jul (CJH).
SWP lst Thornhill 2 May (SS). 4 Glen Buckie 15 May (DT). Family L.Ard Forest 6 Jul (CJH). 2M Milour Moor 15 May, Pr+3Y Glen Tye 17 Aug (WRB).

*STONECHAT *Saxicola torquata (b,w)*
Still few signs of sustained population increase
F M Slamannan (Jawcraig) 22 Nov (FH).
S Pr+imm Kippen Muir 22 Oct (DT).
SWP 2 Thornhill 10 Jan & 2 Feb (CJH). 1 Glenogle 2 Jul (JT). Pr Hutchison dam 15 Nov (WRB).

WHEATEAR *Oenanthe oenanthe (B)*
Under-recorded as breeding in C, S, SWP (Ed).
F 8 Skinflats 2 May (AB). M Kinneil 17 May, 1 on 5 Sep (GO RS). Sev ad & juv Shippytrouty ridge 26 Jun (CJH). Last near Skinflats 11 Sep (MVB)
C 1 Coalsnaughton 13 May (WB). 1 Tullibody Inch 14 Aug (CJH).
SWP 2 Milour Moor 2 Apr, Pr L.Doine on 4th, 2 Ashfield on 7th (WRB EAJ). 2 Callander 7 Apr (DOE). 6 Braes of Balquhidder 8 May (DT). Frequent on Ben Leabhainn (Glenogle) 2 Jul (JT).

*RING OUSEL *Turdus torquatus (b)*
C&S No records - are they extinct on Ochils & Gargunnocks ? (Ed).
SWP 1 Monachyle Glen 2 Apr (DOE). Pr + 2M singing Rhuveag 8 May (DT)

BLACKBIRD *Turdus merula (B,W)*
F 1 Skinflats Apr-May imitated Spotted Redshank (WRB).
S M still feeding fledglings Stirling 5 Aug (D&RJ). Early song at Airthrey 12 Dec (WRB).
SWP Max Dunblane 14 in Nov (BH). 8 taking haws Ashfield 20 Dec (WB).

FIELDFARE *Turdus pilaris (W)*

F 150 Avonbridge 2 Apr, 120 Slamannan 10 Mar & 200 there on 16 Oct (AMcI).Skinflats: 57 on 24 Apr; 251 on 18 Oct, 500 on 19th, 658 on 21st & 269 on 28th, 30 on 19 Nov (AB GO). 48 Higgins Neuk 18 Dec (DF).

S lst at Kippen 13 Oct, 100 on haws 24 Nov (D&RJ). 1000 Stirling 19 Oct (WRB). 100 ->SW Carron Valley 26 Oct (NB). 100 Sheriffmuir 29 Dec (NB).

SWP 110 Lecropt 3 Jan (MVB) & 100 Drip Moss 16 Jan (DT); last 40 Blairdrummond 2 Apr (MVB) & 50 Cromlix 23 Apr (BH). 300 Kinbuck 4 Apr, 20 ->NE Ashfield on 9th & 300 on 16th; 500 -> NE Dunblane 16 Oct, 800 on 17th & 2000-> SW (3hrs) 25th, 250 on 6 Nov (WRB). 50 Dunblane 19 Oct & 100 on 2 Nov (BH). 300 Flanders Moss 20 Nov (DT). 110 Lecropt 5 Dec & 180 on 18th (MVB NB).

SONG THRUSH *Turdus philomelos (B,W)*

Under-recorded as breeding (Ed)

F 1 Higgins Neuk 18 Dec (DF). 1 on weedy sand below HWM Blackness 23 Feb (CJH).

C Max 3 Devon transect in Jan, 5 from 16 Feb (CJH).

S Song Stirling 23 Feb (D&RJ).

SWP Return Ashfield 8 Feb, 3AoT, last on 9 Dec (WRB). 1 Dunblane in Jan & Dec (BH). Max 3 Thornhill transect Jan-mid Feb, 9 on 2 Mar (CJH).

REDWING *Turdus iliacus (W)*

F Skinflats: 8 on 11 Oct, max 100 on 19th (AB GO).

C 150 Devon transect 16 Feb & 110 on 1 Mar (CJH).

S 300 Stirling 19 Oct & 40 on 24th (WRB).

SWP 55 Blairdrummond 2 Apr & 90 ->W on 16th (MVB). 1 Cromlix 23 Apr (BH). lst Kippen 4 Oct (MT). 17 ->SW Dunblane 8 Oct (MVB). 5 ->SW BoA 9 Oct & 70 ->SW on 1 Nov (CJH). Taking rowans L.Ard Forest 11 Oct (NB). 200->NE Dunblane 16 & 17 Oct, 100 on 19th (WRB BH).

MISTLE THRUSH *Turdus viscivorus (B,W)*

Under-recorded (Ed)

F 2 Garbethill 3 Mar (AMcI).1 Skinflats 18 & 19 Oct (GO).

C 7 on Devon transect 19 Mar (CJH).

S 28 Airthrey 18 Aug (MVB).

SWP At Dunblane Jan, Apr, Oct-Dec (BH).

*GRASSHOPPER WARBLER *Locustella naevia (b)*

Seems to have become scarce in last few years (Ed)

F 1 singing Carronshore 29 Apr; Skinflats 27 Apr to 18 Jul (AB GO RS).

C 1 Alloa 19 May (WB).

SEDGE WARBLER *Acrocephalus schoenobaenus (B)*

Under-recorded as breeder (Ed)

F Skinflats: lst on 30 Apr, 4 on 3 May, 11 on 8th; still singing 2 Aug, last on 8th (AB GO). 1 Higgins Neuk & 1 Kinneil 24 Jul (DF CJH).

C 1st Cambus 13 May, 2 AoT (WRB CJH). Sev Alva Pools 23 Jul, 8

Tullibody Inch 14 Aug (CJH).

S 2 Bandeath 7 May (DMB). Migrants Airthrey 4 & 11 May, 5 Sep (MVB).

SWP 1 L.Dhu (Rusky) 1 May (DT). 4 AoT Ashfield-Kinbuck 20 May, last on 21 Aug (WRB). 2 AoT Teith (Kilmahog) 24 May (CJH).

*LESSER WHITETHROAT *Sylvia curruca (?b)*

S M singing Stirling (Broomridge) 28 May to 5 Jul in dense scrub with much hawthorn, no F seen (JT DT).

WHITETHROAT *Sylvia communis (B)*

F M Skinflats 30 Apr, 5 May, 4 on 8 & 15 May, last on 8 Aug (AB GO). 1Kinneil 7 May (GO). 3 AoT Jupiter WG from 18 May (WRB).

C lst Cambus 18 May (WRB). 2 Pr Gartmorn, 4 Pr Devon Way (MC). Sev Alva Pools 23 Jul (CJH).

SWP lst Dunblane 13 May (BH). 4 AoT Kilmahog 24 May (CJH).

GARDEN WARBLER *Sylvia borin (B)*

F 2 Wallacebank Wood 15 May & 1 Union canal (Brightons) on 27th (AMcI).

SWP lst L.Achray 1 May. 2 AoT Ashfield & 5 AoT Barbush-Laighills 25 May; 1 with Willow Warblers Ashfield 2 Aug (WRB). 1 AoT Kilmahog 24 May (CJH). 1 Dunblane 14 Aug (BH).

S 1 Airthrey 9 Aug feeding on Gean berries, with 20 Blue Tits (DMB).

BLACKCAP *Sylvia atricapilla (B)*

Under-recorded as breeder (Ed)

F 1 Wallacebank Wood 15 May (AMcI). F Bo'ness 30 Mar (RS) - ? wintered, Ed.

C M Cambus 1 May (WB).

S lst Stirling 29 Apr, 2 Allan Water on 30th (WRB). 1 BoA 8 Oct (DMB).

SWP 1 Dunblane 14 Aug (BH). M Thornhill 16-30 Dec (B.Howe).

WOOD WARBLER *Phylloscopus sibilatrix (B)*

C lst Gartmorn 26 Apr, 2 Pr bred Cowpark & 3 prs Woodhill (MC). 4 Dollar Glen 4 June (WB).

S 2 Allan Water 30 Apr (WRB).

SWP Singing Glen Lochay 6 May. 3 Rhuveag (Balquhidder) 8 May (DT). 1 Lake of Menteith 16 May (AB). AoTs widespread around Aberfoyle & east shore of Lake of Menteith19-20 May (HEMD). 5 nests found Trossachs (16 in 1993), average success (HR).

CHIFFCHAFF *Phylloscopus collybita (B)*

F 1 Wallacebank Wood 15 May (AMcI).

C lst Gartmorn 1 Apr (MC).

S 2 Airthrey 7 Apr (MVB). 4 Plean CP 15 Apr (DT). 1 Stirling 8 May, brief song on 3 Oct (DT).

SWP 1 Lake of Menteith 1 Apr, separate site 13th (DT). 1 L.Ard Forest 11 Apr, 1 Lake of Menteith 16 Apr (CJH). 1 Dunblane 15, 17 Apr (WRB

MVB). 1 L.Dhu (Rusky) 1 May (DT).

WILLOW WARBLER *Phylloscopus trochilus (B)*

F 1 Jupiter WG 20 Apr (WRB). 2 Kinneil 23 Apr (GO). 2 Skinflats 23 Apr, 4 by 27th, last 16 Sep (AB GO). 1 Carronshore 24 Apr (AB). 1 Falkirk 3 May (AMcl).

C 12 Tullibody Inch 14 Aug, many in reeds (CJH).

S 1 Airthrey 22 Apr, 1 BoA 23 Apr (DMB MVB).

SWP lst Ashfield 13 Apr, party of 12 on 2 Aug, last 3 on 21st (WRB). 1 Lake of Menteith 16 Apr (DT). lst L.Venachar 24 Apr (SS), Strathyre on 27th (EAJ). lst Dunblane 1 May, last on 14 Aug (BH). Abundant Glen Lochay 6 May. No change in summer records on Blairdrummond transect (CJH).

GOLDCREST *Regulus regulus (B,W)*

Under-recorded (Ed)

F Skinflats: present through year, song from late March, with tit flocks from mid Aug (AB). 1 Kinneil lagoon 30 Jan - in solitary conifer in willow scrub(DT).

C Only 6 recorded in 51 km of transects Tillicoultry Jan-Mar (CJH).

SPOTTED FLYCATCHER *Muscicapa striata (B)*

Under-recorded (Ed)

C 3 Dollar Glen 25 May (SH).

F 1 Skinflats 14 May (GO), 1 on 4 Sep (AB).

SWP 1 Ashfield from 20 May (WRB). Sev L.Voil N shore 12 Jun (CJH).

PIED FLYCATCHER *Ficedula hypoleuca (b)*

SWP Singing two sites Glen Lochay 6 May. 2M Balquhidder 8 May (DT). 1 AoT Aberfoyle (Dounans) 19-20 May (HEMD). 51 Prs at Trossachs colony reared 280Y (HR).

LONG-TAILED TIT *Aegithalos caudatus (B,W)*

F 8 Union Canal Brightons 3 Jan (AMcl). 10 Skinflats 19 Oct (AB.

C Max 9 on 8.5 km transect Dollar 19 Mar (CJH).

SWP 17 Dunblane 5 Sep (MVB).15 Allan Water 30 Nov (WRB). 6 on nuts Dunblane 19 Feb & 24 Sep; 5 Braeval 2 Sep (NB).

COAL TIT *Parus ater (B,W)*

C 28 on 51km transect Tillicoultry Jan-Mar, none on similar route S of Thornhill (CJH).

SWP Less frequent on spring transect Blairdrummond than last year (CJH). 6 Dunblane 27 Oct - emptied 300gm sunflower seed holder in 2hr (NB).

BLUE TIT *Parus caeruleus (B,W)*

Under-recorded (Ed)

F 2 Pr fledged Y from wall nests Falkirk (FH).

SWP At Trossachs nestboxes 20% fewer than 1993 but good breeding successs (HR).

GREAT TIT *Parus major (B,W)*
Under-recorded (Ed)
SWP At Trossachs nestbox colony occupation up 50% but 33% of nests failed (HR).

TREECREEPER *Certhia familiaris (B,W)*
Under-recorded (Ed)
C Only 4 records in 51 km transect Tillicoultry Jan-Mar (none on equivalent count S of Thornhill CJH).
SWP 1 Gartmore 5 Dec (NB).

*GREAT GREY SHRIKE *Lanius excubitor*
S 1 Carron V Forest 6 to 19 Feb (JM), (presumably the 1993 bird stayed over New Year, Ed).

JAY *Garrulus glandarius (B,W)*
Under-recorded as breeder in SWP (Ed)
F 1 Kinneil Wood 2 Jan, 1 Bo'ness garden 27 Mar & 2 on 18 Nov (RS).
C Absent from Jan-Mar transects Tillicoultry & Thornhill (SWP) (CJH).
SWP In Apr at L.Venachar, two sites L.Ard Forest (CJH).1 Lake of Menteith 31 May (BHc). In Autumn at Queen Elizabeth Forest Park,Torrie, Mid Lix, Blairdrummond (NB). 2 Kippenross 15 Dec, Cromlix 22 Dec (WRB).

MAGPIE *Pica pica (B,W)*
Its abundance around Stirling is not necessarily noted in the west and east of the area (Ed).
F 8 Brightons 3 Jan (AMcI).
C Scarce Tillicoultry, only 4 in 51 km transect Jan-Mar (CJH). 8 Cambus 10 Mar (WB).
S Large roost Airthrey, 76 on 14 Feb (MVB).
SWP Only 12 records in year Dunblane (NB). Scarce S of Thornhill - only 4 in 67 km transect Jan-Mar (CJH). Now widespread Braes of Doune, up to 270m (WRB).

JACKDAW *Corvus monedula (B,W)*
Under-recorded (Ed)
SWP 70 Ashfield through year (WRB). Roost at Dunblane Hydro 45 on 14 Oct, 38 on 2 Dec (NB).

ROOK *Corvus frugilegus (B,W)*
Rookery counts: BoA(N), 18 in decid, 79 in pines. BoA(S) 153 ; Witches Craig 45; Myretoun 65. Total 360 (339 in 1993). 27 at Kincardine in Menteith (CJH). 162 Bannockburn (Balquhidderock) on 24 Apr (DT)
S Departure from roost over BoA to N at 08.20 on 20 Jan (CJH). At one rookery tree in Stirling there was a part built nest on 16 Feb, 6 by 21st & 5 complete on 2 Mar, 11 complete by 26 Apr; only 8 nests visible after leaf-fall in Nov (DT).
SWP 800 Sheriffmuir 29 Dec (NB).

CARRION CROW *Corvus corone (B,W)*

F Carrion/Hoodie hybrid Kinneil 12 Oct (DT).

C Av 89 per 8.5km transect Tillicoultry Jan-Mar, max flock 68 Dollar 16 Feb (CJH). Cambus roost: 190 on 16 Jan, 45 on 7 Apr, 140 on 22 Dec (CJH).

SWP Av 75 per 9.5km transect Thornhill Jan-Mar (CJH). Hoodies: Thornhill 10 Jan, 2 Feb,18 & 19 Apr, 12 Dec (CJH SS); in breeding range at Stronachlachar, L.Venachar, L.Lubnaig, Balquhidder (NB).

RAVEN *Corvus corax (B,W)*

C 3 Blairdenon 12 Jun (SH).

S 2 Territories checked, 2 pairs present but only one successful, rearing 1Y (PSA). 1 AoT Ballochleam (JM). 2 Airthrey 14 Jan & 3 Oct (DMB). 3 Carron V Forest 2 Apr (DT).

SWP 18 Territories checked, 16 with pairs & 2 unoccupied; of 11 successful pairs 7 reared 19Y - breeding success slightly lower than 1993, possibly due to snow in early spring covering carrion (PSA). Out of usual breeding area: Pr L.Rusky 9 Apr (DT). 2 L.Ard Forest 26 May, 3 on 30 Jul & 1 on 5 & 30 Aug (CJH). 3 Hill House 4 Apr, 3 Cromlix 23 Oct (WRB)

STARLING *Sturnus vulgaris (B,W)*

C Tullibody Inch roost: 900 on 11 Oct, 300 on 13 Nov, 50 on 22 Dec (CJH); an unprecedented 20,000 in this area at roost time 6 Nov (MVB).

S 400 at roost Stirling centre 31 Jan, 2 Feb, 100 on 22nd, last noted 28 Mar (CJH DT), not present before Christmas but 200 at end year (WRB DT). 1 with a long, curved bill Stirling 16-19 Jan (D&RJ).

SWP Max 72 on 9.5km transect Thornhill Jan-Mar (CJH).

HOUSE SPARROW *Passer domesticus (B,W)*

Under-recorded (Ed)

C 40 Alloa 14 Aug (CJH).

TREE SPARROW *Passer montanus (B,W)*

F 35 Skinflats 17 & 18 Feb, 4 on 3 Aug, 25 on 3 Dec & 68 on 31st (AB DOE GO RS). 3 Powfoulis 26 Feb (DF). 1 Dunmore 12 Jun (SH). 2 Letham Moss 5 Jun (DMB).

S 2 Cambuskenneth 9 Mar (KPA). 2 Gartmorn 17 Apr (WB).

SWP 45 Drip Moss 20 Feb. 122 Lecropt 26 Feb (MVB) *(probably record flock for area, Ed).*

CHAFFINCH *Fringilla coelebs (B,W)*

F 70 Skinflats 7 Jan (AB). 300 Slamannan 15 Nov (AMcI).

S 270 BoA 9 Oct (CJH).

SWP 300 Drip Moss 13 Feb & 400 on 20th (MVB DT). lst Song Thornhill 25 Feb (SS). Abundant in Monachyle Glen by 30 Mar (DJP). Spring numbers as 1993 on Blairdrummond transect (CJH). 75 Kinbuck 22 Oct (WRB).

BRAMBLING *Fringilla montifringilla (W)*

F 400 Carronshore 2 Jan, 10 on 15th (AB). 5 Skinflats 7 Jan & 1 on 5 Feb (AB). Kinneil: 10 on 1 Jan & 12 on 9th, 6 on 29th, 30 on 26 Feb (GO RS DT).

C 14 Gartmorn Jan-Feb (MC). 40 on stubble Clackmannan (no Date (WB).

SWP 2 with Chaffinches Dunblane 9 Oct (BH). 2 Ashfield 17 Oct, 6 Kinbuck on 22nd (WRB). M singing in oak-birch wood 10 Jun - not seen on 12th & 30th Jun or 18 Jul.

GREENFINCH *Carduelis chloris (B,W)*

F 70 Kinneil 1 Sep (CJH).

S 250 Kippen 18 Sep (MT).

SWP 100 Kippenrait 4 Sep. 400 Kinbuck 8 Oct (MVB). Max 10 Dunblane Feb & Apr (BH), 8 at feeder 13 Nov (NB).

GOLDFINCH *Carduelis carduelis (B,W)*

F 60 Zeneca on 8 Feb & 75 on 19th (J Falconer). Skinflats: Max 40 on 16 Jan & 13 Mar, 30 on 16 Apr, 10 on 3 May, 25 on 20 Nov & 22 on 31 Dec (AB GO). 8 Airth shore 19 Feb, 27 Myot Hill 9 Oct; 10 Shippytrouty 26 Jun (CJH).

C 15 Longcarse 15 Jan; 15 Cambus 2 Aug & 50 on 30th, 20 on 13 Nov (CJH).

S Through summer at Airthrey & 2 sites BoA (CJH).

SWP Bred Ashfield & 20 on 23 Oct (WRB). 4 Glenogle 2 Jul, Callander 5 Jul (JT). 10 Dunblane 9 Oct (BH).

SISKIN *Carduelis spinus (B,W)*

F 3 Skinflats 29 Mar & 2 on 8 Apr (GO).

C Max 39 on 8.5km transect Tillicoultry 1 Mar (CJH).

S 10 Airthrey 14 Jan; 20 BoA 17 Aug (DMB). lst of autumn in Stirling garden 30 Oct (D&RJ).

SWP 200 L.Katrine 29 Mar (AMcI). Only 2 in 67 km of transect S of Thornhill Jan-Mar (CJH). 2 Braes of Doune (Hill House) 15 May. 4 ->N Ashfield 16 Oct (WRB). A few L.Ard Forest 21 Mar, widespread by 26th. Frequent L.Venachar 16 Apr (CJH).

LINNET *Carduelis cannabina (B,W)*

F 35 Airth Shore 15 Feb; 150 Kinneil 15 Jan & 350 on 30th; 150 on 18 Dec (MVB CJH). 100 Skinflats 3 Aug (DOE).

S 70 in rape stubble Gogar 9 Oct (CJH).

SWP 200 Drip Moss 20 Feb (MVB). Thornhill: 150 on 2 Feb & 160 on 17th (CJH); 200 on 11 Nov (D&RJ). 100 Kippenrait 4 Sep (MVB). 10 Ashfield 3 Mar, sev AoT; singing Sheriffmuir 2 Oct (WRB). 500 Kinbuck 8 Oct (MVB).

TWITE *Carduelis flavirostris (b,W)*

Under-recorded as breeder (Ed)

F Kinneil:10 on 1 Jan , 30 on 2nd; 5 on 29 Oct & 23 on 31 Dec (GO RS).

Skinflats: 70 on 16 Jan, 30 on 27 Feb & 25 on 20 Mar; 9 on 19 Nov (AB GO RS). 70 Airth shore 19 Feb; 15 on 26 Nov (Sea Aster crop poor, CJH). 25 Dunmore 4 Dec (MVB).

SWP 2 Ashfield 3 Mar; 1 over Cromlix 15 Nov (WRB). 1 Thornhill 26 Jan (CJH).

REDPOLL *Carduelis flammea (B,W)*

F 15 Skinflats 30 Oct (AB).

C 30+13 Dollar 1 Mar (CJH). 5 Gartmorn 19 Nov (WB).

SWP 60 Inverlochlarig 10 Feb (DOE). Present in oakwoods L.Katrine 10 Jun & L.Voil 12 & 30 Jun. 1 Doune Ponds 25 May (CJH). 2 in plantations Braes of Doune 15 May and at Ben Leabhainn 2 Jul; Pr Ashfield all summer, 5 from 22 Oct -5 Dec (WRB JT).

BULLFINCH *Pyrrhula pyrrhula (B,W)*

C 23 in 68 km transect Tillicoultry Jan-Mar (CJH).

S Pr feeding on seed of Hypericum at Stirling 1-11 Feb (D&RJ).

SWP A few Dunblane through year, eating Nettle seeds in Dec (BH), also L.Ard Forest, Blackwater Marshes, Invertrossachs (NB CJH). 9 Barbush 18 Oct (WRB).

COMMON CROSSBILL *Loxia curvirostra (b,W)*

S 4 (display flights) Carron V Forest 6 Feb, 30 on 12th, song heard (DF GO RS), 1 singing on 14 Jun (CJH), 7 on 3 Jul (DMB).

SWP L.Ard Forest: 6 on 26 May, 7 on 25 Jun, 2 (singing in flight) on 5 Aug (CJH). 3 L.Venachar 16 Apr (presumed juv begging for food) (CJH). 4 L.Rusky on 23 Jan, 9 on 5 Feb, 10 on 18 Dec (DT). 2 (1M singing) Torrie Forest 16 Jan, 5 on 1 May; 11 Gart Wood 16 Jan (DT).1 Braes of Doune 4 Apr, 5 Hutchison 22 Nov (WRB).

HAWFINCH *Coccothraustes coccothraustes (?b,?w)*

No records received

SNOW BUNTING *Plectrophenax nivalis (W)*

No records received - presumably no observers on the winter hills (Ed)

YELLOWHAMMER *Emberiza citrinella (B,W)*

F 25 Skinflats 6 Feb & 20 on 5 Mar, 8 on 9 Apr (AB GO). 17 Higgins Neuk 18 Dec (DF).

C 190 Gartmorn Jan-Feb (MC). 18 Longcarse 30 Jan (CJH).

SWP 90 Lecropt 3 Jan & 60 on 5 Mar (MVB). 10 Dunblane 9 Mar (BH). 21 on 9.5km transect Thornhill 17 Feb & 17 on 2 Mar. 8 on 4 Km transect Blairdrummond May-June (CJH).

REED BUNTING *Emberiza schoeniclus (B,W)*

F 52 Skinflats 17 Feb, mainly in stubble (RS).

C 4M singing Cambus Pool 13 May, probably only 2 regular AoT (WRB CJH). 7 in plantation Hutchison 22 Nov (WRB).

SWP 8 on 9.5km transect Thornhill 19 Mar (CJH).

*LAPLAND BUNTING *Calcarius lapponicus*
1 Skinflats 27 Feb (RS).

*CORN BUNTING *Miliaria calandra (b,w)*
F M Singing Powfoulis 26 Jun & 12 Jul (WRB GO). M singing 1.5 km SW 5 Jun & 24 Jul (DMB DT). Not found at Powbridge site.

Wildfowl Report (1994-95)

Neil Bielby is now organiser (Central Region) for the inland waters part of the Wetlands and Estuary Bird Survey (WEBS) and reports that 113 sites were covered by 14 counters. This is 93% of sites larger than 1 Ha and below 300m elevation. Table 1 shows the Regional totals for all species counted each month. Webs covers ducks, swans and geese plus grebes, Cormorants and other typical wetland species such as Herons, Coots and Moorhens, however the bottom row shows grand totals for ducks only. Note also that the Webs season covers a whole winter, in this case from September 1994 to March 1995. Mallard are by far the most numerous duck, as would be expected, and maintain a steady total population until a drop off in March, there is however an August build up (see systematic list) that is necessarily not in the WEBS data. By contrast, Teal, Wigeon and the diving ducks show an increase through the autumn. There is a suggestion of a late autumn influx of Coot whereas both grebes are scarce in mid-winter. Other records in this report show that Canada Geese are not really absent in autumn.

Table 1. Monthly Totals for all sites, Sep 1994 to Mar 1995

Species	Sep	Oct	Nov	Dec	Jan	Feb	Mar	Total	Mean
Little Grebe	42	24	17	15	2	27	24	155	21
Gt Cr Grebe	31	28	13	1	2	5	22	102	14
Cormorant	15	84	42	44	21	24	13	243	34
Heron	31	24	42	25	24	35	19	200	28
Mute Swan	99	83	122	96	100	87	115	702	100
Whooper Swan	0	1	47	50	45	59	40	242	35
Canada Goose	0	0	0	17	26	32	25	100	14
Wigeon	89	521	364	361	936	862	434	3567	510
Teal	171	259	308	178	346	319	168	1749	249
Mallard	2198	2548	2642	2693	2671	2541	1166	16459	2351
Pochard	57	117	225	120	290	266	106	1181	169
Tufted Duck	179	329	206	340	342	387	367	2150	307
Goldeneye	22	62	122	157	161	150	271	945	135
Goosander	46	41	55	78	57	88	66	431	61
Coot	190	355	610	556	373	311	293	2688	384
Total Ducks	2592	4232	4532	4483	5176	4924	2871	—	4167

Table 2 compares some of the major sites, showing, for all Webs species, the mean monthly counts, the number of species (season total), the mean counts excluding Mallard, and also the mean of the three largest counts ("Regular counts", which give a better idea of the typical peak wintering population). This table clearly shows the importance of Gartmorn Dam in all respects, how Airthrey Loch is dominated by Mallard and how relatively small artificial waters such as Gart Loch and Quarry Loch can contribute as much as far larger sites as Carron Valley Reservoir and Lake of Menteith. Sites not in Table 2 but with notable Regular Counts include Loch Laggan (Kippen), Loch Macanrie, Blairdrummond Safari Park and Marl Loch (Argaty).

Table 2. Wildfowl statistics of some Major Sites

Site	Mean	Mean - Mallard	Mean of 3 max	Number Species
Gartmorn Dam	905	638	1375	16
Airthrey Loch	455	125	513	10
Carron V. Res.	219	157	358	17
Gart Loch (Callndr)	216	178	364	10
Lake of Menteith	149	129	270	16
Quarry L. (Blairdr)	148	-	244	13

The main WEBS contributors to these data were A. Ayre, B. Barker, M. V. Bell, N. Bielby, W. R. Brackenridge, M. Callan, W. McEwan, M. Verel.

BOOK REVIEW

The University of Stirling, Beginnings and Today. R. G. Bomont. Stirling University. 1995. 160 pp. ISBNs Hbk 1-875769-0265 £20; Pbk 1-875769-0273 £14.95.

Before returning after 22 years as University Secretary Bob Bomont with Bank of Scotland sponsorship stepped in with this welcome work following the sad death of Professor David Waddell who had been engaged on an official history. Here we have from a closely involved participant rather than a historian, a valuable brief account of the promotion, selection, planning, leading to the start of the University; a tribute to the 1000 or so devoted people who contributed to its successful launch and early years, particularly to that academic visionary and innovator, the first Principal Tom Cottrell. From about page 50 we have a selection of photographs and notes about buildings, people and special occasions on to 1994. From page 133 are useful reference appendices of committees, sponsors, appeal subscription lists, and the students and staff of the first year 1967.

Further to this book it should be noted that we published Professor Trainer's important paper *Twenty Five Years On: the Impact of the University* in *FNH* volume 16. University Jubilee Issue, pp. 71-76; also previously was Mark Brownrigg's thesis of 1971 on the impact of the *University's first five years*, published by Scottish Academic Press. On the Airthey Estate might be noted a substantial study in *FNH* volume 9, pp. 81-111, *Airthrey Roads, Captain Haldane's Magic Roundabout* by Mackay and Angus.

BOOK REVIEWS AND NOTES (Naturalist)

Extinct Encounter. Dr Spooner, organizer at the Butterfly Conservation Society for eastern Scotland has reported sightings of an apparent March Fritillary (*Euphydryas aurinia*) at Birkhill Wood, Clackmannanshire (NS 9493). This rare butterfly, akin to the small pearl-bordered fritillaries, is said to have been last reported in this area in the *Alloa Advertiser* of 1864. As yet waiting full verification the report is published in the *Clackmannanshire Field Studies Society Newsletter* 24(1), October 1995, pp 23-4.

Scottish National Heritage – recent publications include:

Boglands – Scotland's Living Landscapes. 20pp. ISBN 1-85397-102-0. £2. A well-illustrated introduction.

Natura 2000 – guides to the 1992 EC Habitats Directive – *Marine Environment* and *Terrestrial Environment*, each 20pp.

Well illustrated on protecting Europe's most valuable habitats and species.

Loch Lomond to Stirling – Landscape Fashioned by Geology Series. 1995. SNH and BGS. 27 pp. ISBN 1-55397-119-7. £2.

Well-produced booklet by M. Browne and J. Mendum, with several illustrations by Pat Macdonald, and the D. Grinly based drawings of the landscape of the Ochils across the contents pages. This work is an attempt to show how diversity in landscape reflects the underlying geology developed over millions of years, with the recent geological past ice's role in shaping the scenery; this being a classic area for viewing its dramatic effects. A full study of Clackmannanshire geology by Mike Browne and David Grinly is in progress for *FNH* volume 19.

THE WINTERING BIRDS OF TWO CONTRASTING FARMING LANDSCAPES IN CENTRAL SCOTLAND

C J Henty
University of Stirling

Summary

The wintering birds of two distinct rural areas in central Scotland were studied by making transect counts from November 1993 to March 1994. One transect was in a primarily pastoral area and the second where about half the ground was in arable production. Buntings, sparrows and certain finches were more frequent in the arable district whilst there were more cover haunting passerine species in the pastoral area, consistent with the abundance of tall hedges and woodland. Lapwings, Golden Plover, Pied Wagtails and Song Thrushes were scarce or absent until the late winter or early spring. Preliminary data was collected on the use of hedges and of different types of fields. Both similarities and some differences occur when comparison is made with other studies in the UK and the reasons for some anomalies are discussed.

Introduction

The Forth Valley to the west of the Kincardine Bridge is an area of mixed farmland situated immediately south of the Ochil Hills and the southern and central Highlands and is a major wintering ground for many species of birds. On the Carses of Stirling and Clackmannan farms are arable with pasture, thus the landscape is generally open with little woodland - for example, between Thornhill and the River Forth. By contrast, in the middle Devon valley between Tillicoultry and Dollar there is very little arable and to the north of the River Devon it is possible to find an extensive route that is purely through lowland grazing land and is characterised by high hedges and parkland with small mixed woods and belts of trees. There is little quantitative information for central Scotland on bird communities in winter related to differerent styles of farming, thus I decided to make a detailed study of the birds of these two areas The main question concerns whether a given species is commoner in one farmland type rather than another. Two secondary questions were also addressed: First, does a species use different field types unequally and /or how important are hedges ?. Second, which species show evidence of a mid-winter absence followed by a marked spring return ?.

Methods

Two transects were set out in November 1993 The Devon transect started along the footpath close to the River Devon then skirted the outskirts of Dollar and returned eastward (8.5 Km, altitude range 15-75m above sea level). A suitable transect on the Carse of Stirling was more difficult to design due to lack of access paths but I set out one that skirted south of Thornhill village and used minor roads with little traffic to complete a 9.5 Km transect (altitude range 11-30m above sea level). Six initial transects were made in each area between 10 November 1993 and 17 February 1994, two further pairs of transects in early March and March 19 and 20 were done to examine the issue of spring immigration which is marked in several species that are present in mid-winter only in small numbers.

Observations were made by recording sightings and calls of birds within 200m, this distance was chosen since small birds were the main focus of interest and also because beyond this distance the two areas differed in the extent to which trees obscured visibility. Birds flying over in high and steady flight were considered as commuting (not using the area) and not included in the transect data. I used x8 binoculars and maintained a steady pace with pauses to identify and make notes. Transects were done only on days with no appreciable rain and with moderate or light winds, they were alternated between the two areas and successive pairs were on dates as close together as feasable, however, due to other commitments and spells of bad weather this was only successful (spaces of a week or less) for the 12 transects after the New Year and so the "pairing" has not been used in data analysis. Count data were standardised to a 10 Km basis and t-tests performed on the two sets of eight numbers (in cases where there was very high variability amongst counts a log transformation was applied. No specific predictions were made as to whether any species might be expected to be commoner in one of the areas, thus two-tailed probabilities were used).

The relative extents of woodland plus scrub with trees and also of tall, unmanaged hedges were estimated by measuring on 1:10000 maps the distances along the census bands (200m either side of the transect route) in which the habitats were present. In the arable area an analysis of the main field habitats was made by noting the state of each field as either winter wheat, grass, plough (bare soil) or stubble. Then the length of each field boundary on the transect was measured on a 1:2500 map and each category summed to give an estimate of the percentage extent of each field type. Only small sections of a few fields did not extend from the transect line out to or beyond the 200m recording boundary so the linear measure is a good indication of the relative areas relevant to the transect. Very little change in the nature of the fields occurred until March when some stubble was ploughed and crops in what had initially been ploughed fields had sprouted enough to transfer them into the winter wheat category. The net effect of this was to transfer some stubble (down 23%) to winter wheat (up 18.5%); an overall proportion was calculated by weighting the earlier and later results according to the number of transect counts that were appropriate. The grass fieldtype in the arable area is very mixed, ranging from unmanaged pasture to seeded grass plus the grazed fields that had in summer 1993 been grown tall for hayseed. There was also undersown stubble where the distinction betwen grass and stubble is arbitrary in some cases.

Results

All the major field habitats on the Devon transect consist of grassland, much of it old pasture whereas at Thornhill only about half is grassland with about half of that fairly intensively managed. In both areas sheep and cattle are common grazing species with a few horses. Although some type of hedging is found along most of both routes there is far more cover in the form of tall

Table 1. Frequencies of regular species on Devon (pasture with copses) and Thornhill (open arable) areas. Numbers are average recorded per 10 km of transect.

Species	Devon	Thornhill	Probability
Woodpigeon	22.9	9.3	NS (Ln)
Stock Dove	0.0	3.9	**
Skylark	0.4	87.0	* (Ln)
Meadow Pipit	1.0	14.7	*
Pied Wagtail	2.2	1.4	(S)
Wren	5.6	3.4	NS
Hedgesparrow	8.6	4.5	**
Robin	23.8	5.5	**
Blackbird	38.1	12.6	**
Song Thrush	3.4	2.8	(S)
Fieldfare	10.5	19.6	NS (Ln)
Redwing	60.3	13.7	NS (Ln)
Mistle Thrush	3.0	1.4	NS
Long-tailed Tit	4.6	0.0	**
Coal Tit	4.9	0.0	**
Blue Tit	36.6	5.3	**
Great Tit	24.5	1.8	**
Carrion Crow	87.8	70.7	NS (Ln)
Starling	44.4	74.8	NS
House Sparrow	17.1	30.2	**
Tree Sparrow	0.0	2.8	**
Chaffinch	37.0	64.8	NS
Greenfinch	14.6	8.0	NS
Goldfinch	4.7	2.6	NS
Siskin	13.9	0.4	*
Linnet	0.0	91.1	** (Ln)
Bullfinch	3.4	0.1	**
Yellowhammer	1.9	8.9	*
Reed Bunting	0.0	3.7	**

NS = no significant difference. * = significant. ** = highly significant
(Ln) - T test on log transformed counts due to high variability
(S) - no area comparison due to marked spring arrival
N.b: the total number of records for each area can be found by multiplying the Devon figure by 6.8 and the Thornhill figure by 7.6.
Occurrence of cover on transects:

	Devon	Thornhill	
Woodland / scrub+trees	2.3	0.42	Km
Tall hedge	3.0	1.1	Km

hedges and of woodland or scrub plus trees at Devon, see Table 1 for details. Scattered trees were present along part of the Thornhill route and most of the Devon but quantitative estimates were not made.

Table 1 shows the average frequency per transect, standardised to numbers per 10 Km, for those species that occurred on at least six dates on at least one of the areas; Rooks are excluded from this table since, although seen commonly, their flocks often straddled the 200m observation limit and counts were difficult to replicate consistently. The Stock Dove (*Columba oenas*) occurred only in the arable area even though the Devon transect includes a large area of parkland pasture with many mature trees. More surprisingly, the Woodpigeon (*C. palumba*) does not appear as wintering in larger numbers in the arable, indeed it is on average less frequent there although the difference is not significant due to high variability between counts. Clear arable specialists include Skylark (*Alauda arvensis*), Meadow Pipit (*Anthus pratensis*), Linnet (*Carduelis cannabina*), House Sparrow (*Passer domesticus*), Tree Sparrow (*P. montanus*), Yellowhammer (*Emberiza citrinella*) and Reed Bunting (*E. schoeniclus*). Starling (*Sturnus vulgaris*) and Chaffinch (*Fringilla coelebs*) show indications of a preference for arable, but not to a significant degree, whilst Carrion Crow (*Corvus corone*), Fieldfare (*Turdus pilaris*) and Goldfinch (*C. carduelis*) are notably even handed. Mistle Thrush (*T. viscivorus*) and Greenfinch (*C. chloris*) show no strong differences, nor, and much more surprisingly, does the Wren (*T. troglydytes*). Rooks (*Corvus frugilegus*), Jackdaws (*C. monedula*) and Blackheaded Gulls (Larus ridibundus) were all seen regularly in numbers but often just beyond the census boundaries so that the numbers seen in a given transect depended on the exact feeding site in a very erratic manner; both the corvids were frequent in both areas but the records were not analysed for area comparisons. Pinkfooted Geese (*Anser brachyrhynchus*) were seen on the ground only at Thornhill; although in large numbers they were usually at some distance outwith the censuses. The species that are much more frequent on the Devon transect are no surprise since they are all well known either to feed in trees and bushes or are strongly associated with cover : Hedgesparrow (*Prunella modularis*), Robin (*Erithacus rubecula*), Blackbird (*Turdus merula*), Longtailed Tit (*Aegithalos caudatus*), Coal Tit (*Parus ater*), Blue Tit (*P. caeruleus*), Great Tit (*P. major*) and Siskin (*Carduelis spinus*). There is of course a number of species that occurred too erratically or in numbers that are too small for formal analysis. Of these Sparrowhawk (*Accipiter nisus*), Kestrel (*Falco tinnunculus*), Buzzard (*B. buteo*), Grey Partridge (*P. perdix*), Pheasant (*Phasianus colchicus*), Collared Dove (*Streptopelia decaocto*), Great Spotted Woodpecker (*Dendrocopos major*), Stonechat (*Saxicola torquata*) and Magpie (*P. pica*) were noted on both areas. Two Peregrines (*Falco peregrinus*) and single Merlin (*F. columbarius*) and Twite (*Carduelis flavirostris*) occurred only at Thornhill and Green Woodpecker (*Picus viridis*), Jay (*Garrulus glandarius*), Treecreeper (*Certhia familiaris*) and Goldcrest (*R. regulus*) only on the Devon transect. A Grey Wagtail (*Motacilla cinerea*) wintered by the Devon and one appeared in March on a burn near Thornhill.

There is a difference in the distribution of Fieldfares compared to Redwings although this is not proven in the single species analysis since the higher number of Redwings on the Devon is not quite statistically significant. Overall Redwings outnumber Fieldfares on the Devon by 4:1 but at Thornhill the ratio is just less than 1:3 and an analysis of the percentages from individual transects shows this is significant (t test, $p = 0.012$); this probably reflects the Redwing's preference for foraging near cover. The Wren, though on average more frequent on the Devon, shows no significant preference. This is partly due to the fact that they use the trimmed hedges on arable land and partly to a series of low counts on the Devon transect after mid January, including both March counts; the reason for this is obscure - there is no similar effect in other small insectivorous birds.

Several species show a marked spring arrival. On the arable both Lapwing (*V. vanellus*) and Golden Plover (*Pluvialis apricaria*) were almost completely absent until a number of flocks of both species appeared on March 2nd and 20th. Common Gulls (*Larus canus*) were usually scarce but there were almost 500 on March 2 whilst the first Lesser Blackbacked Gull (*L. fuscus*) was seen on March 1. Oystercatchers (*Haematopus ostralegus*) appeared in numbers by the Devon on March 1 whilst there were 60 Curlew (*Numenius arquata*) there (off transect) on the 19th and 8 at Thornhill on the 20th.

Song Thrushes (*Turdus philomelos*) were noted on both transects in small numbers until a sustained increase occurred from February 16, Pied Wagtails (*Motacilla alba*) showed a similar but later arrival on March 18. No such arrival was seen in Meadow Pipits (Anthus pratensis) whose numbers declined markedly after early February. The best indication of spring movement in Skylarks was from the Devon transect on March 1 when a party of 22 flew high and determinedly, with song, toward the Ochil Hills just to the north. Their numbers on the Thornhill carse were difficult to interpret, they were apparently absent in mid and late January and also in mid (but not early) February, however on January 30 I saw 200 on stubble in an area between my study routes; this suggests that Skylarks may undertake marked local movements in midwinter that can both simulate and obscure more general and long distance passage. I suspect that such a local movement produced very few Rooks at Devon on December 24, there was a very hard frost but the opportunity of easy feeding on a rubbish dump within easy flight distance. Carrion Crow records were generally divisible into those involving pairs and those involving flocks, there was always a large flock by the sewage plant near Dollar whilst those on the Thornhill carse seemed more mobile and often included a Hooded Crow. One general problem of interpretation arises since the first Devon count was on November 10 whereas the first Thornhill count was on December 20, however an abortive pilot transect on nearby arable on November 11 showed large numbers of Skylarks and Fieldfares and the presence of Yellowhammer, Tree Sparrow and Reed Bunting, as well as the absence of typical hedge species; thus there is no reason to suppose that the absence of a full count on arable in November affected any major results. Both transects included a small section skirting the edge of a village and this shared feature may slightly reduce the overall differences, but there it would not exaggerate any of the differential frequencies that have been described.

Habitat selection by field type

This analysis is limited since only a fraction of records could be certainly allocated to a particular habitat - I had to be sure a bird was actually foraging in a field, not simply perched in a tree at the field edge.

Table 2 shows for a few common open country species the preference (Jacobs Index, as in Tucker 1992) of a species for each fieldtype, taking into account their relative extents; the index varies from zero (no like or dislike) up to 1 for exclusive preference and down to -1 for total avoidance. No statistical analysis was possible but the largest positive index for each species has been highlighted to emphasise the main positive preferences.

Table 2. Preference Indices for various fieldtypes

		Fieldtypes & extents (%)			
Species	Tot.N	Grass	W.Wheat	Stubble	Plough
		(60)	(19)	(16)	(5.2)
Skylark	(370)	-.84	+.22	**+.70**	+.29
Meadow Pipit	(107)	**+.81**	-1.0	-.47	-1.0
Fieldfare	(69)	**+.48**	-.01	-1.0	-1.0
Starling	(324)	**+.72**	-1.0	-.27	-1.0
Rook	(552)	-.48	-.90	**+.81**	-1.0
Jackdaw	(58)	-.39	-1.0	**+.78**	-1.0
Carrion Crow	(515)	+.03	-.63	**+.32**	+.16
Linnet	(367)	-1.0	**+.87**	-1.0	**+.69**

It is apparent that most species showed at least one marked preference, with stubble being the most often preferred habitat though not for Meadow Pipit , Fieldfare and Starling, which are grassland specialists, and Linnet, whose high ratio for winter wheat is due almost entirely to one flock in one particular field. The liking of Skylarks and Linnets for ploughed ground is due to records from one freshly ploughed field that also attracted Chaffinches and Reed Buntings. On a small sample both Stock Doves and Yellowhammers frequented stubble but for the latter species this underestimates the use of old pasture where the birds were wary and difficult to assign. An attempt was made to assess the importance of hedges as food sources in the arable area by also recording when a bird was sighted foraging in a hedge or initally present there, ie with no reason to suppose it had gone there as a response to disturbance. However, the combined problems of being quite sure of the accuracy of such categorisation and the scarcity of typical hedgerow species meant that few data could be obtained. Not surprisingly, none of the species in Table 2 was ever recorded as foraging in hedges - even Fieldfares and Redwings, since no berries remained. By comparison 60% of Blackbirds foraged in hedges as opposed to open fields, all of the Wrens and Robins and almost all the Hedgesparrows and Blue Tits (one of the former explored the road and one of the latter was in stubble).

Discussion

There are relatively few quantitative studies of the total bird community of farmland in winter, however, the results of this study are broadly consistent with the general remarks of O'Connor and Shrubb (1986) and of Lack (1992) for the UK and of Bryant (1994) for central Scotland. Also the lists of species commonly found on arable areas versus those specially associated with cover in the studies of Arnold (1983) and of Tucker (1992) are similar to the present results. Nevertheless there are some surprising features in this study and some detailed differences from previous work.

Woodpigeons are classically found in large flocks on arable farms (Murton 1965) but were distinctly scarce on my Thornhill counts although I noted 500 only 10 Km away; it is probably significant that these birds were feeding on a leafy crop, possibly oilseed rape, such crops are commonly found on many arable farms and considered important for midwinter survival (Inglis, in Lack 1986), but there were none on my transect. Thus longer transects would be needed to sample Woodpigeons adequately on my arable locality. Tucker found that almost all his species preferences were for permanent grass and not for any stage of tilled land (the one exception being Magpie for stubble). Quite likely there are preferences for permanent grass in my areas, since I could not easily make the distinction from ley grass but informally often noted that birds were on old pasture, which Tucker found to harbour high populations of invertebrates. Rooks in Aberdeenshire use stubble to a marked degree (Feare et al 1974) so it may be that Scottish stubbles are a more generous source that those of Buckingham and thus attract corvids, Skylarks and the less common species mentioned previously. Holyoak (1968) found that grain was a predominant food component in corvids with much of it coming from stubbles. Tucker's and this study agree on the preference of Fieldfares and Starlings for grassland, my Meadow Pipits noticeably fed on grass in one particular field amongst grazing sheep but this apparent association with sheep could be a chance effect. Total avoidance of a fieldtype (Jacobs Index -1.0) was not infrequent, 10 instances, and particularly notable in winter wheat and plough, but how far it simply reflects a preference for alternative and easily available habitats is not clear. However, only Skylark and Linnet, which can feed on small seeds, show any liking for winter wheat and plough. Other species may be unable to find suitable food in these intensively worked fields since large grains are absent and, as noted by Tucker, invertebrate food is often very scarce. Hence definite avoidance seems likely in some cases.

In this study the small passerines which were typical of the Devon have similar associations with high hedges and copses in Arnold's work: it is particularly interesting that he also found Wrens quite commonly in arable areas provided there were ditches with hedges, this combination being not uncommon around Thornhill. There were no signs from local transect work near Stirling that this species was scarce in the spring of 1994 and the data in the Atlas of Wintering Birds suggest that my winter data for the Devon was not unusual, hence the relatively uniform distribution of Wrens over widely different farming areas may be normal. Tucker found that thrushes, the four species also in this study, occurred mainly in fields enclosed by hedges and suggested this was an anti-predator tactic against hawks. This seems plausible but together with my data would predict that Redwings are particularly vulnerable. One final point of difference from the two English studies is that both found Song Thrushes to be commoner (relative to Blackbirds) than I did. Together with my early spring influx this is consistent with the finding (Snow, in Lack 1986) that Scottish Song Thrushes are markedly more migratory than those in southern England. However, since the earlier studies a winter population index for Song Thrushes has declined by 50% (Garden Birds Study, BTO News 194) so the midwinter difference between Scottish and English farms may no longer hold. Arnold noted that the numbers of finches and buntings in a quadrat were correlated with the area of house gardens in the quadrat and its surroundings, this was not true for House Sparrows which correlated with the area of woodland. The last unexpected result is not reflected in this study: on both transects it was noticeable how House Sparrows were common along the fringes of the two villages but otherwise were restricted to the six farms and outlying homesteads in the arable area though not present in five similar sites within the pasture-parkland.

Conclusion

This study has generally confirmed what is widely understood to be the typical community of arable farmland but has also thrown up a number of unexpected features, some of these may be peculiarities of the particular fields investigated but others seem likely to be connected with regional differences.

Acknowledgements

My thanks go to the University of Stirling, Dept. of Psychology, for providing word processing and computing facilities and to D.M.Bryant and H.Robb for lending books from their private libraries.

References

Arnold, G. W. (1983). The influence of ditch and hedgerow structure, length of hedgerows, and area of woodland and garden on bird numbers on farmland. *Journal of Applied Ecology*. 20, 731-750.

Bryant, D. 1994. Birds. in Corbett et al. Central Scotland – Land, wildlife, people. Forth Naturalist and Historian, University of Stirling.

Feare, C., Dunnet, G. M., and Patterson, I. J. (1974). Ecological studies of the Rook in north-east Scotland: food intake and feeding behaviour. *Journal of Applied Ecology*. 11, 867-896.

Holyoak, D. (1968). A comparative study of the food of some British Corvidae. *Bird Study*. 15, 147-153.

Lack, P. (1986). The atlas of wintering birds in Britain and Ireland. Poyser.

Lack, P. (1992). Birds on lowland farms. HMSO.

Murton, R. K., (1965). The Woodpigeon. Collins.

O'Connor, R. J. and M. Shrubb, (1986). Farming and birds. C.U.P.

Tucker, G. M., 1992. Effects of agricultural practices on field use by invertebrate-feeding birds in winter. *Journal of Applied Ecology*. 29, 779-790.

Figure 1 Picture with hedges and copses at Devon Way information site.

Figure 2 Open pasture-arable near Thornhill.

BOOK REVIEWS AND NOTES (Naturalist)

A Scottish Strategy for Environmental Education. Statement of Intent by the Secretary of State for Scotland. Scottish Office. 1995. 36pp.

While this Government response to the Working Party report *Learning for Life* appears positive, emphasizing greater Scottish Office awareness and establishing a subgroup on Education for Sustainable Development, it is disappointing that the basic National Advisory Panel has not been implemented.

"**MFMM**". Scottish Ornithologists' Club. 1994. 88pp. ISBN 0-9524610-0-5. £4.95 incl. p.&p., cheques payable to SOC Clyde Branch (Available: D. Clugston, 14 Rosewood Avenue, Paisley, PA2 9NJ).

This small publication is a long overdue selection from the thousand plus weekly articles written for the *Glasgow Herald* between 1954-1974 by the man behind the distinctive initials – the late Professor Matthew Fontaine Maury Meiklejohn, *ornithologue extraordinaire.*

On picking-up their Saturday *Herald*, ornithological readers would invariably flick through to MFMM's short piece before ever turning to the newspaper's coverage of national and world affairs. Although most of the articles were devoted to his perambulations in search of birds – which included excursions to Loch Lomonside and the Forth Estuary – it would be a mistake to think that MFMM's humorous pen was confined to this one subject alone. Complete with the original complementary sketches by J.B. Fleming, this is not a book to be read at the one sitting, but to be dipped into for moments of quiet pleasure.

J. Mitchell

Birds of the Endrick Mouth, Loch Lomond: an update of the annotated checklist to January 1990. John Mitchell *in Scottish Naturalist* 106, 1994, part 1, pp 3-30.

The first edition with description and history of the area was in the *Scottish Naturalist* of 1984, 3-47 and summarized known records to January 1980. These next 10 years have sixteen species added, and changes in status of those already recorded – some 230 species have been recorded on one or more occasions.

Old Cornerstone Workings in Dunbartonshire and West Stirlingshire, with Notes on their Associated Flora. John Mitchell *in Glasgow Naturalist* 22, part 5, 1995, pp. 485-494.

This paper may interest readers who remember Mackay's "Limestone Working: forgotten Stirlingshire industry" paper in *FNH* 2, 81-105.

FORESTRY IN THE OCHILS

Syd House
Forestry Authority

This article presents an overview of the role of forestry in the Ochils, touching on the history of woodland cover; the development of the woods and forests we have today and how they are made-up; how forestry operates in the countryside in general; current developments and issues with the opportunities they represent; and finally the potential for establishing new woodlands.

History of Woodland in the Ochils

The Ochils we see today are predominantly an open landscape with rolling hills and long views. But it is a landscape much altered by people as they settled into the area after the last Ice-age 10,000 years ago (Keymer 1981). When those first hunter-gatherers arrived they would have been, in common with the rest of Scotland, in a largely wooded landscape. Something like 70-80% of the country was covered with trees. These natural forests would have been predominantly broadleaved, with oak, ash and elm on the bottom of the glens and fertile hills, giving way to birch, rowan and willow on the poorer and more exposed soils. Only the tops of the hills around 500m, and wet bogs and peats (e.g. Maddy and Alva mosses), where even alder and willows could not grow, would be open ground unsuitable for tree growth. Those early settlers would have faced a situation not unlike that facing the Colonists arriving on the North American Eastern seaboard in the 18th and early 19th century - extensive forests over miles and miles.

What then happened to these forests and how did we get to the woodland landscape we see in the Ochils today (Proctor 1994). Basically the story is not dissimilar to today's forest clearances in the tropics. The history of the forest is principally one of exploitation by man. While the early hunter-gatherers probably lived more or less at one with the forest using it mainly as a source of food, heat and shelter, as more people arrived pressure on the forest grew greater, and a more settled pattern of agriculture led to forest clearance. By the time the Romans arrived much of the forest had already disappeared although there was still enough to convince the Romans that Scotland was a land of great forests. Thereafter the clearance continued apace, mainly for land for agriculture. With the introduction of sheep and an intensive pastoral system from the Middle-Ages onwards, the demise of extensive woodland cover was assured. And it wasn't only the onslaught of man that the woodlands faced. There is also considerable evidence to suggest that natural conditions conducive to woodlands have deteriorated over the same period with a poorer and wetter climate leading to peat formation on the wetter soils. Scotland, at the extreme North West of the Eurasian land mass, is already at the edge of that range, so any small fluctuations either way can have an enormous impact. But again, tree clearance could contribute to a raised water table, hence man in this respect contributed to the formation of bogs and peat.

In summary therefore, we have an area once extensively covered by forests and woods but now predominantly clear of trees for a variety of reasons. There are some remnant examples which may be natural, if enormously altered, descendants of that original woodland cover. These are situated mainly in gorges and glens, such as Alva and Dunning, or alongside watercourses such as the Queich and Dunning Burns, where access was difficult for both man and sheep. Some have survived because of their value as a source of timber and raw material or because they provided shelter and winter pasture for livestock. Good examples include the oakwood at Ruthven Mains near Kincardine Castle at Auchterarder.

Whilst the history of these woods has generally been one of decline, their ability to recover and regenerate when grazing is excluded is remarkable and bears witness to the tenacity with which these woods have survived. It also highlights the potential for these woods to once again extend onto their natural areas, and encouragingly there is considerable interest in bringing these woodland remnants into positive management and extending their range.

In the 18th and 19th centuries Scotland was hugely influenced by the 'Great Improvers' who sought to radically increase the productivity of the land by introducing scientific methods of husbandry. The rural landscape we know today owes much to their influence. In forestry terms this was a period when landowners recognising the value of productive woods started thinking more seriously about managing their existing woods and planting new ones. This was the beginning of regularised forest management and the design and creation of Estate Woodlands such as those at Airthrey (now within the grounds of Stirling University), Dupplin (near Perth), Freeland and Rossie (around Forgandenny) and Gleneagles. These woods featured the introduction of new species to Scotland which offered a wider scope for planting than our native species. These introductions included beech, sycamore and lime amongst the broadleaves, and larch, spruce, silver firs and the Douglas Fir amongst conifers. As a result of these introductions, particularly the conifers from North America, the potential for enhanced tree growth was realised. Indeed Scotsmen, such as David Douglas from Scone, were major influences in these new introductions and many of the estate owners in the area vied with one another in their enthusiasm for tree-planting. An example of such enthusiasm was that of the Earl of Kinnoull at Dupplin Estate where in 1870 he laid out a 10-acre pinetum using virtually every known conifer introduced to Scotland at that time. Some of these still survive today towering above the rest of the wooded skyline as you look south from the A9.

Accordingly when the Forestry Commission (FC) was set-up in 1919 to create a strategic reserve of timber for times of national emergency, and with the majority of tree planting was undertaken with these introduced conifers, leading directly to the wooded landscape we see today. The first FC plantings took place in Dunning Glen in the late 1930s and continued for forty years to create new woods as in Glensherup and Pitmedden. After World War II increased incentives encouraged private landowners to establish new woods. Although there are several older woods, most of these new privately-owned plantations date from the 1960s, 70s and 80s, and the predominance of conifers was then a function of forestry policy geared to one major objective - timber production for industry, and largely located in the uplands to fit in with agricultural policy. In recent years forestry policy has diversified to enable the creation and management of woods for a whole variety of reasons - popularly known as multipurpose forestry. To reflect this the incentives have been changed to recognise the wider range of demands that the nation as a whole expects for public subsidies. The current woodland constituent within the Ochils consists of around 15,000 ha of woodland (equivalent to 20% of the land cover). Most of this is conifers with a high proportion under 30 years old. Smaller areas of more mature conifers are on lower ground, generally on traditional estates. Broadleaved and mixed woodlands account for around 1/5th of the wooded areas and include some much altered ancient semi-natural remnants of the once widespread natural woodland cover. Forest Enterprise manages only around 2,000 ha within the Ochils, the remaining 13,000 being privately owned.

How Forestry fits into the Rural Scene

From a period of decline at the turn of the century when Britain imported virtually all its timber requirements, the establishment of new forests has encouraged a home-grown timber industry which can meet around 15% of demand, and is set to double this over the next 20 years. What we have now is a thriving home-grown industry supporting businesses and jobs like those at Caberboard at Stirling and W P Murray's sawmill at Forgandenny. Forestry has been the major method of diversifying land out of agriculture (mainly rough grazing in the uplands) this century.

How then does the forestry world operate?

(a) The state, through the Forestry Commission, plays a key role in two ways. In does this firstly as a land manager buying land and establishing and managing woodlands - known now as Forest Enterprise (FE), and secondly as Forestry Authority (FA) promoting forestry through training, research and incentives to private landowners; it also regulates the felling of trees and monitors their health. Three years ago these separate roles of the Forestry Commission were defined more clearly - Forest Enterprise now operates at arm's length from the Forestry Authority and requires approval from the latter before undertaking planting or felling operations.

(b) Forestry activities along with agriculture are exempt from most of the normal planning procedures of local authorities. This is in recognition of the traditional role of these interests in the countryside and the need for a certain amount of flexibility and freedom in their management. In forestry and woodland matters there is a well-established consultation process which the Forestry Authority operates when approached by private landowners for permission and grant-aid to either plant or fell trees. Such proposals now trigger full consultation or notification with local authorities, River Purification and Salmon Fishery Boards, Regional Archaeologists, Scottish Office Agriculture and Scottish Natural Heritage. Consultees can object to proposals and can sustain those objections through a series of different levels of appeal right up to the secretary of State. Since the introduction of the Woodland Grant Scheme in 1988 the Forestry Authority has received and approved over 1,000 applications to fell or plant trees within Tayside, Central and Fife and in that period there have been no sustained objections - all issues were resolved at local level!

Issues Raised in Relation to Woods and Trees

There are a number of reasons why forestry has excited comment:

(i) General environmental awareness has been increasing in recent years leading to greater public interest in all aspects of our environment including land use change. As the biggest cause of such changes, new woodlands are bound to attract attention.

(ii) New forests have often been situated in the uplands in visually prominent areas.

(iii) The methods of establishing new woods have evolved to become more industrial and intensive, e.g. ploughing and draining with heavy machinery and the extensive use of single species monoculture in growing timber as a raw material for industry. Such methods have not always been as sympathetic to landscape considerations nor of access to hill tops for walkers, or watercourses for fishermen as we would now require.

(iv) Agricultural policy required that the best land understandably was retained for agriculture. This meant that forestry inevitably was pushed onto the uplands which, precisely because of their unimproved nature, were of the highest conservation value.

(v) Recently afforested land was (particularly under the previous tax regime) often owned and managed by individuals who, unlike the upland farmers, were not local and often viewed as adversely affecting the structure of the local community.

(vi) With the advent of acid rain, conifer forests were perceived as exacerbating the effects of industrial pollution with a consequent effect on fishing and water interests. In some catchments forests were seen as potentially reducing the amount of water available for reservoirs and public water supplies due to their greater ability to intercept rainfall for evaporation back into the atmosphere rather than draining into the water bodies.

Within these perceptions there is undoubtedly a great deal of substance which foresters have needed to listen to. One of the pleasures or curses, depending on your viewpoint of being involved in forestry, is the timescale over which it takes place. Unlike farming where a crop planted one year can be changed the next, trees once planted tend to be in place for 50 to 60 years - action to cut down early or replace can be very expensive. Inevitably trees planted 30 years ago cannot by themselves take account of the many changes that have taken place since, so what happened then is still available to be seen now.

Issues Within the Ochils

Here the forestry issues which have tended to be raised have centred on -

(i) the impact on landscape with straight lines and large single species blocks, for example through Dunning Glen and in the area above Dollar.

(ii) access: a belief that large conifer plantations blocked access onto traditional open ground.

(iii) the effect on water - there being several large public water supplies in the Ochils.

Fishing interests have also been concerned at what was then felt to be inappropriate planting. Tied in with these has been a general resistance to change in the traditional, at least in memory, open nature of the Ochils from some outside force which was not accountable to anyone at least as far as the layman was concerned. These were and are genuine feelings held by a large number of people, not just particular to the Ochils, but held for a large part of the Scottish uplands.

So what are the current developments in relation to woods and forests, and what is the outlook for the Ochils?

Recent Developments

Firstly there is a continuing Government policy to expand the nation's area of woodland. However, since 1985 there has been a broadening of the types of woodlands being created, with a greater emphasis on - farm woodlands (helping reduce agricultural subsidies, and the more fertile nature of the ground allowing a more diverse type of forestry); native woodlands (recognising their inherent natural value); and woods established for community benefit.

The major incentive available to private landowners is through the Woodland Grant Scheme (WGS), administered by the FA, which was introduced in 1988 when tax-incentives were withdrawn from forestry planting. Grants are available to establish different types of woodlands and include a whole suite of supplements designed to encourage perceived public benefits, e.g. grants for broadleaves are higher than for conifers. There are substantial supplements for planting on 'better' land (taking it out of productive agriculture), and for creating woods near towns and villages, involving the local community in setting-up the establishment of the wood as a community asset. Further grants provide for public access to woodland and for managing semi-natural woodlands to conserve their unique heritage value.

All of this represents an enormous evolution of forestry policy since the 1970s and early 80s. The evidence of this increased diversity is clear, with the area of broadleaves planted increased dramatically. There has also been a deliberate switch to target existing woodlands and enhance their environmental benefits through such things as public access, conservation interest and landscape enhancement.

Secondly there is now a suite of environmental guidelines which all parties receiving grants or permissions from the FA must comply with. Coupled with this is the requirement for formal environmental assessment for new planting proposals.

Thirdly the introduction of Indicative Forestry Strategies has sought to direct new woodlands to areas identified as 'Preferred' or 'Potential' for such proposals whilst highlighting 'sensitive' areas where substantial new woods may be inappropriate or where there is a need to address particular new issues. They have helped to avoid conflict.

Fourthly the consultation process has been widened to encourage greater openness and public involvement, including the introduction of a public register of WGS applications.

Lastly, but by no means least, there has been a greater dialogue on all sides to understand how woods and forests fit in to our countryside, and how new proposals can be accommodated to take account of all interests. Within the Ochils this new approach has been translated into action in a number of interesting ways. These include -

(a) Reshaping and expanding native woodland remnants: at Alva Glen an organisation called Scottish Native Woods is working in partnership with the local farmer to regenerate through the WGS, a remnant native woodland. The Tayside Native Woodland Initiative, a partnership of various bodies including the FA and Scottish Natural Heritage (SNH), has been surveying the native woodlands to assess their condition and encourage landowners to bring them into positive management and secure their future. Several woods in the Ochils have already been surveyed and assessed.

(b) New community woods have been established around the fringes of the Ochils at Gartmorn and Muckhart with the aim of involving local people and helping improve the immediate environment of communities which serve as gateways to the hills.

(c) New large-scale woodlands have continued to be established but have incorporated a more diverse approach, e.g. a new 150 ha integrated farm forestry scheme at Ardargie Estate includes a substantial element of native species as well as commercial conifer and broadleaf. Other smaller integrated farm forestry schemes have been agreed for areas east of the M90 at Balvaird and Letham.

(d) FE has produced long-term design plans for their woodlands demonstrating their commitment to multipurpose forestry. These are subject to public consultation before approval by the FA. One of these plans was viewed by and discussed by the Friends of the Ochils on their field visit to Dunning Glen.

(e) On the access front the owners and managers of several privately-owned mainly conifer blocks have agreed to open up their woodland areas for informal public access for which they will receive FA grants. These areas include Greenhills on the Dunning Glen road, Dollar Estate above Dollar and Blackhill just north of Kinross. The agreed proposals will also result in improvements in conservation, landscaping and watercourse management.

Other woods open to public access include the NTS-owned Dollar Glen and the Woodland Trust's Woodhill Woodland at Alva - both financially aided by the FA.

Opportunities

These are firm proposals and represent positive action. There are a number of potential opportunities which are actively being explored. These include -

(i) Planting broadleaved trees alongside watercourses and feeder burns to Loch Leven. This would help reduce phosphate run-off from agricultural land and help treat the problems of algal blooms in the loch and the impact they have on a valuable economic resource. FA has been working with SNH, FRPB and local farmers to promote this. A priority would be to improve areas where conifers have been planted too close to water courses in the past.

(ii) Encouraging landowners to provide access to woodland areas or at least allow walkers to pass through. In our experience to date we have been pleasantly surprised by the genuine willingness of landowners to respond to such approaches. The FA does not know of any immediate problems in the Ochils, but would like to know of any problems and will attempt to broker some solution using its incentives package.

(iii) Thirdly there are significant opportunities for expanding the woodland area within the Ochils using the diverse approach outlined above. That means a place for both broadleaves and for conifers. Such woods properly sited and planned can contribute to the overall variety of the Ochils, continue to provide new material to industries, and help provide jobs and enhance our future by securing a productive and viable countryside fulfilling the wide diversity of objectives we all wish or it.

References

Keymer, Richard. 1981. The extent and compostion of native woodlands in Central Region. *Forth Naturalist and Historian* 6, 83-96.

Proctor, John. 1994. Vegetation and Flora - history since the Ice Age; chapter in *Central Scotland, land, wildlife, people*, pp. 43-56. Also chapters Soils, Aquatic Life, and Nature Conservation. Forth Naturalist and Historian.

Book Reviews and Notes (Historical)

The Hillfoots in Old Picture Postcards. Ian Murray. European Library, "Back in Time" Series. 84 pp. 1995. ISBN 90-288-6096-7. £9.95.

From a brief introduction to the natural characteristics of the area, the author leads us into 76 pages of photographs and historical notes through places along the Ochils from Blairlogie to Dollar. While many may be familiar to local history buffs some are less known, e.g. Old Mill Menstrie, Middleton Kerse, The Lipney, Myreton House, Thompson's Temperance Hotel, Hillfoots Picture Palace, The Tillicoultry Flood, Opening of Dollar Station, Cowden House. The well-researched notes highlight social, industrial and recreational events and features, and succeed in achieving some of the memories the Hillfoots should carry "to refresh itself, and to open the eyes of other travellers".

The Noblest Jacobite of All. A. K. Smith. Privately printed. 1995. 21 pp. £3 including p&p from the author at 16 Katrine Crescent, Callander FK17 8JS, or from Bell Library, Perth, or University Bookshop, Stirling.

James Drummond, 3rd Duke of Perth was he; member of the Society of Improvers and planner of the village of Callander the Duke, targetted as a prime participant by Prince Charles, narrowly and fortuitously escaped a planned kidnapping by the Government's Murray of Ochtertyne before sucessfully joining the Prince as one of the first and most important supporters of the '45 Rising. The author outlines the campaign and the Duke's involvement – adding appendices on Jacobite Perthshire and Trossachs. The Duke, wounded at Culloden, died aboard the French warship *Mars* after leaving Scotland on 4th May, 1746.

Stirling, the Royal Burgh. Craig Mair. John Donald in association with Stirling District Libraries. 1995. 308 pp. ISBN 0-85976-420-6. £9.95.

This is a paperback reprint of the 1990 hardback book which we reviewed in *FNH* volume 13, pp. 107-8. Originally in 1990 £13.95, then (1993) remaindered £7.50, it has unfortunately been out of print for some years. A straightforward history for general reading, putting Stirling into the context of Scottish history, it is presented attractively for reading, and for appreciating the numerous and pertinent illustrations. Much has happened since the 1960s, and our book *Central Scotland – land, wildlife, people* and a number of papers in our annual *FNH* supplement and update some aspects of the Stirling story. We do, however, look forward to another Mair-like read on Stirling into the year 2000.

THE FOUNDING OF THORNHILL IN 1696

G. A. Dixon

> "One of the most striking pieces of evidence for later seventeenth-century Scottish history is the dramatic increase in the number of burghs of barony and licensed market centres, especially after 1660" (1).

Just over a century prior to 1660 only 143 such centres had been established; in less than half a century onwards to the Union 346 were authorised (2). The recent discovery in the Central Regional Archives of a detailed early Georgian inventory of the earliest feu charters of Thornhill in Menteith throws an informative spotlight upon a new settlement which was both more than a licensed market centre and less than a burgh of barony, and was brought into being in the very months when the expanding pre-Union Scottish economy was plunged into crisis by the first of the nationally catastrophic harvest failures of the later 1690s.

Now about to celebrate its tercentenary, the new Thornhill – or Thorniehill, as it was sometimes spelt in its earliest days – was founded by Archibald Napier of King's Boquhapple, a great-grandson of John Napier of Merchiston, the famous Scottish mathematician who invented logarithms, the greatest pre-computer aid to computation. Only months before his death in April 1617, John Napier had bought from Archibald Edmonstone "his twenty merk lands of [King's] Boquhaple with the pertinents in the Stewartry of Menteith and Sheriffdom of Perth" (3). This little estate descended through Robert Napier, the second son of the mathematician's second marriage, and Robert's eldest son, Archibald, to the latter's elder son, also Archibald, who succeeded to King's Boquhapple while still a minor, in the early 1660s, and married Annabella Linton in May 1679 (4). Like his father and grandfather, he lived in troublous times, and on 24th May 1689 the Scots Parliament:

> "considering how necessar it is for ther Majesties service and for the securitie of the country of Monteith and places adjacent on both sydes of the river of Forth, that the foords and ferries of the said river above Stirling be guarded and secured ... Do grant full power warrand and commission to Archbald Naper of Boquhaple, and James Stewart younger of Ardvorlich to raise and convocate in armes, the number of three hundered men or more ... who are well affected to the present government ... to guard and secure the saids foords ... And to seaze upon and secure all persones, who are lyable to the suspition of being dissaffected, or in opposition to the government, As also to guard and secure the said Countrie and bounds from thifts robberies depredationes oppressiones and others violencies to be committed upon any of ther Majesties peacable subjects And for that end the Estates doe authorize them to garisone such castles, and houses in the saids bounds as shall be most convenient for the said service" (5).

By the early 1690s, however, the not particularly glorious revolution was over, and in the relatively calm and prosperous interlude that followed, Archibald Napier of King's Boquhapple turned his thoughts to giving his estate the economic heart it lacked, a village. Immediately upon his eastern boundary lay the tiny hamlet of "The Six Merk Lands of Easter Boquhaple commonly called Noriestown" (6), in a bend of the Cessintully Burn, upon whose "Knowhead" (7) there were built three successive churches, the second of which, after an extraordinarily protracted campaign commencing in 1652 (8), became the seat of a new quoad sacra parish in 1878 (9). Successive Nories – latterly, Gavin, James, Alexander, Gavin and David – had owned Easter Boquhapple (though not wholly uninterruptedly) since the 15th century (10), but although it came to accommodate the ecclesiastical centre for the isolated western section of the parish of Kincardine-in-Menteith, Norrieston offered it no economic centre. In the early 1690s the nearest authorised fairs or markets were in Doune, 4 miles as the crow flies to the east; Kippen, 3½ miles to the south; Port of Menteith, 5 miles to the west, and Cambusmore, 4 miles to the north (11). Archibald Napier, accordingly, sought to strengthen his estate's economy with Parliamentary assistance.

On 17th July 1695, in a unique burst of economic optimism, the Scots Parliament authorised the holding in 40 different locations in Scotland of no fewer than, in total, 85 annual fairs, 18 weekly markets and 3 annual markets (12). Among them there was enacted:

> "in favours of Archibald Naper of Balquhaple ... that in all time coming there be four free fairs Setled and Established yearly at the Toun [i.e., fermtoun] of Kings Balquhaple in the Parochin of Kincardin ... One wherof upon the twentie day of October, the other upon the fourteenth day of November the other upon the first tuesday of March and the other upon the second tuesday of June with a weekly Mercat therat upon thursday".

The MS inventory of c1727 adds the names of those fairs: Margaret's, Martinmass, Lentron and Hill's, respectively, "each ... to continue the Space of 8 days". The fairs were free in the sense that they were unfettered by burghal trading rights, but the right to exact "the Toll & Custom of the said Fairs" was granted "to the said Archibald" (13).

Having obtained his new fairs and market on the very day that the Scots Parliament, so great was its confidence that Scotland could more than feed its own population, granted subsidies for grain exports (14), Napier then prepared his next move, the actual foundation of a village. As its site he selected the gently rising ridge running westwards from his eastern boundary just west of Norrieston Church. The street of his new settlement was to run with a rise of about 25 feet (15) east-west along the crest of the ridge, and with a standard frontage of 21 ells (some 65 feet) and plot length of 66 ells (some 203 feet), though in the event half and one-and-a-half frontages were also to be permitted. The 65-foot width of the standard building plot strikingly foreshadowed the 60 to 65-foot frontages found in many of the hundreds of Georgian planned towns and villages laid out with the aid of land surveyors and populated with the aid of press advertisements between the 1730s and the 1830s (16).

In the 1690s, Napier had neither newspapers to advertise in, nor land surveyors on hand to give his new settlement right angles, rigid symmetry and dead straight building lines. The attractions of the site, however, and the freedom inherent in the feu rights on offer, were sufficient to bring forward 15 settlers ready to receive their charters on the founding day, 10th February 1696 (17) – a total which compares favourably with, for example, the 20 settlers attracted in its first three years to the most abundantly documented, and one of the more successful, of all Scotland's Georgian foundations, New Grantown in Strathspey (18).

All but one of the 15 settlers chose building plots fronting to the "peice ground appointed to be the Street in Thorniehill of Kings Boquhapple" (19), the exception being "James Spittall in Kings Boquhappell for himself & as actorney for & in name of Agnes Mckean his spous and of Andrew, Alexander, & John Spittalls his sones". The Spittalls' plot was substantially larger than the others, lay across the eastern tail of the hill against the Norrieston boundary and incorporated some existing buildings which might well have previously been occupied by Mrs. Spittall's late father. The want of any properly surveyed feuing plan for the new village is nowhere more obvious than in the frustratingly vague definition of the bounds of this easternmost of the Thornhill plots:

> "All and heall the houses & yairds laitly possest be umquhile Bartholemew Mckean, and of additione therto the hous to be built att the west end of the said houses To the nixt adjacent few which is to be the compleit martch on the west and from the wester Gavel [i.e., gable] thairof straight north The number of thrie scoir eightein elnes, and from the north west Nook of the said March running in ane streight lyne be north the dub, eastward to the North nook of the yaird, on the east syde of the dub being upone the march of Noristoun, and from thence douneward upon the martch betuixt Noriestoun & Kings Boquhappell untill it come to the head of the bog, and from thence westward, on the south syde till it come to the south east nook of Andrew Chalmers yaird, And that straight north to the easter Gavill of Andrew Chalmers few" (20).

If, however, one takes the existing cross lanes at no. 47 Main Street on the north and no. 50 on the south as "the wynd[s] Lyeing South and Northward throwgh the toune of Thornehill" (21), it is possible to assemble a basic feuing plan using the plot dimensions and bounding proprietors' names given in the relevant registers of sasines (RS). On the south side of the street the entire stretch between the cross lane and the south-western boundary of James Spittall's feu was taken as follows by first-day feuars (running from west to east, giving plot sizes in ells, feuars' previous addresses, and occupations where known):

1) James Law, 21 x 66, King's Boquhapple, – .

2) John Spittall, 10½ x 66, King's Boquhapple, shoemaker.
3) Donald McLaren, 10½ x 66, King's Boquhapple, weaver.
4) Duncan Smith, 21 x 66, Bridgend of Doune, – .
5) Robert Sands, 21 x 66, Cardross, – .
6) John Maxwell, 21 x (?66), Murdieston, notary public.
7) Robert Paterson, 21 x 66, Burnside, – .
8) James McCulloch, 21 x 66, Murdieston, – .
9) Andrew Chalmers, 21 x 66, Mill of Cessintully, – .

The only other first-day feuar on the south side of Main Street appears to have taken a plot west of the cross lane:

10) John Mitchell, 21 x 66, Wester Boquhapple, – .

On the north side of Main Street, all four first-day feuars took contiguous plots running eastwards from the cross lane (the remaining frontage, of unspecified length, eastwards to James Spittall's north-western boundary, was feued off in 1699):

11) Thomas Paterson, 21 x 66, McOrriston, – .
12) William Paterson, 21 x 66, Boghall, – .
13) William Mitchell, 31½ x 60/66, King's Boquhapple, – .
14) Andrew Mitchell, 10½ x 60, King's Boquhapple, – (22).

Apart from Smith and Sands, both from points some 4 miles distant, all the initial settlers in Thornhill came from places lying within a mile of the site of the new settlement.

The apparent curtailing of the north-eastern feus may have reflected the alignment of the existing W-E highway as it cut eastwards from what is now the junction of the A873 and the B822 towards the north-westwards curve of the Norrieston Churchyard boundary. As late as 1706, "the present high road" lay "Sixtie four elns" north of Main Street at a point two plots west of the cross lane (23).

In addition to the building plots themselves, Archibald Napier granted to his Thornhill feuars:

> "Libertie to ... Quarrell Craig, faill, Divot and Morter", in other words, to quarry stone, dig turf and make mortar, "for building, repairing and upholding the houses and yaird to be built theron Within the most convenient bounds of the Lands of Kings Boquhaple, and free ish and entry for Loading the samine therto As alsoe ... for Leading thair peats yearly wpon the Common Cairt way Betwixt the said house to be built, and the moss of Kings Boquhaple" (24).

The feu duty, payable each year at Martinmas, was set at the rate of two merks (£1'6'8 Scots) per standard 21 x 66-ells feu, and feuars were required:

> "to Answer at the head Courts to be holden by the said Archibald Napier and to attend him when called to the Kings host with Sufficient cloaths and arms under the pain [i.e., penalty for failure] of twenty pounds" Scots (25).

That after the first surge of feuars early in 1696 the flow shrank to a trickle was merely one of many symptoms of the economic and social disaster then striking Scotland. The 1695 harvest had failed and normally in such circumstances the human food-supply crisis would peak during the following spring and early summer, to be relieved as the new harvest came to hand. Several successive harvests failed, however, in the late 1690s (26) and great loss of life ensued. For example, in 1698:

> "the harvest became altogether disastruous, first by great winds and thereafter by rains, yea and storms of snow &c. ... the plague of famine ... occasioned so great a mortality ... that the year ... [1700] ... so was most calamitous ... multitudes died for want of bread ... People die[d] in the streets and high wayes in great numbers ... in some paroches at least the one half died for want" (27).

In Thornhill after 10th February 1696 only five more feus were granted during the founder's lifetime (he died in the closing days of 1699 (28)): to George Harrison in February 1699 in the NE gap between the plots of Andrew Mitchell and James Spittall, to two John McCullochs in December 1696, to Archibald McCulloch in February 1699 and to Alexander Fletcher 10 months later; all four of the latter edged the village westwards beyond the cross lanes, on both sides of the street (29).

The "Ill Years" at the turn of the century were the last straw for a family and estate already in debt (30). On 28th March 1704 Archibald Napier's eldest son, Alexander, was served heir to his late father and on 17th April following he sold King's Boquhapple, including the superiority of Thornhill, to George Drummond of Blair Drummond for the sum of £30,958'17'8 Scots (28 and 31). Although several of the existing feus changed hands in the interim, Drummond had, by Thornhill's 15th anniversary in 1711, granted only one new feu there to James Drummond, on 24th May 1706, at the western extremity of those on the north side. The definition of the latter's feu boundaries suggested that the new laird did not share the founder's preference for a standard plot size:

> "All and heall the number of twenty six elns of ground of front westward from the corner of Alexander Fletchers few ... with the number of Sixtie four elns of ground northward from the said Corner ... to the north west Corner of his yaird with the number of Fiftie one elns of ground westward from thence upon the present high road and with eightie four elns from thence Southward to the Street of Thornhill joining to the South march of this few" (32).

It was not of course only feuars and their immediate families who lived in the new settlement. Those tenants occupying rented property are now beyond tallying, but successive Thornhill schoolmasters, for instance, none of them a feuar, are detectable as witnesses in the surviving documentation as early as 11th December in the founding year: "Mr William Dun schoolmaster in Thornehill" witnessed a charter then, and its formal implementation on the following day (33). By April 1702, "Mr Robert Muschet" was "Schooll master at Thornhill" and by May 1706 "Mr Robert Steuart" occupied that position (34).

Within the next 50 years, "the village of Thornhill having four fairs and a weekly mercat", as Alexander Graham of Duchray laconically described it in 1724 (35), experienced little or no growth. The earliest Drummond estate rental located, that for crops 1743-54, lists 27 feuars (36), only one more than the total in 1711 (37). The post-'45 military map of mainland Scotland c1750, in so far as its detail can be trusted, shows the village extending little further west than the two cross lanes (38). Thornhill's age of expansion, during which it swept over and around the crest of The Hill, lay yet further in the future, during the second half of the 18th century, as it filled out with tanners, handloom weavers, and other tradespeople (39). The decline of rural industries in the 19th century hit Thornhill hard, but the capacity for survival which brought it in its earliest years through the greatest environmental disaster of recent centuries has in this century carried it forward to celebrate its tercentenary as a thriving community.

References

1. Lynch, Michael: "Scottish Towns 1500-1700", introduction to "The Early Modern Town in Scotland", ed. Lynch, M. (1987), p. 25.
2. Whyte, Ian D.: "The Growth of Periodic Market Centres in Scotland 1600-1707", *Scottish Geographical Magazine*, vol. 95, no. 1 (April 1979), pp. 13-26.
3. Central Regional Archives (C.R.A.): PD119/1/7, pp. 89-90.
4. Smith, J. G.: "Strathendrick and its Inhabitants from Early Times" (1896), pp. 177-79, 187-88.
5. "The Acts of the Parliaments of Scotland" (A.P.S.), vol. IX (1822), p. 92.
6. PD119/1/7, p. 214.
7. W[ ], G.: "Norrieston, Thornhill", *The Stirling Antiquary*, vol. 1 (1893), pp. 134-36.
8. C.R.A.: CH2/723/2, under 14th July 1652.
9. *Stirling Journal and Advertiser*, 29th August 1879, p. 2, and "Abstract of the History of the Intended Erection at Norriestown drawn from the Records of the Presbytery of Dumblane": C.R.A.: CH2/1227/6/1.
10. Balfour Paul, J. (Ed.): "The Register of the Great Seal of Scotland A.D. 1424-1513" (1984), pp. 126, 505; Fraser, W.: "The Red Book of Menteith" (1880), vol. 1, p. 312; PD119/1/7, pp. 213-15. David Norie disponed half of the lands of Norieston to James Muschet in 1688: *ibid.*
11. Marwick, J. D.: "List of Markets and Fairs now and formerly held in Scotland" (1890), pp. 43, 77, 91 and 30, resp.
12. A.P.S., *ibid.*, pp. 498-503.
13. PD119/1/7, p. 94.
14. A.P.S., *ibid.*, pp. 458-59.
15. O.S. Perthshire sheet CXXXI.3, revised 1899.
16. See, e.g., Houston, J. M.: "Village Planning in Scotland, 1745-1845", *The Advancement of Science*, vol. V, no. 18 (July 1948), pp. 129-32; Smout, T. C.: "The Landowner and the Planned Village in Scotland, 1730-1830", pp. 73-106 in Phillipson, N. T. and Mitchison, R. (eds.): "Scotland in the Age of Improvement" (1970), and Lockhart, D. G.: "The Planned Villages", pp. 249-70 in Parry, M. L. and Slater, T. R. (eds.): "The Making of the Scottish Countryside" (1980).
17. Two other feuars' charters were also dated that day, for plots at existing houses just beyond the western margin of the hill: RS59/8, fos. 461, 468.

18. Scottish Record Office (S.R.O.): RHP13911.
19. S.R.O.: RS59/8, fo. 480.
20. *Ibid.*, fo. 456.
21. RS59/9, fo. 29.
22. 1)-14) resp., RS59/8 except where stated otherwise: fo. 466; 505, PD119/1/7, p. 120; *ibid.*, p. 124; RS59/10, 270; 467; PD119/1/7, p. 117 (despite Maxwell's being a notary, his title remained unregistered in either the particular or the general registers of sasine at his death prior to February 1710 (RS59/12/2, 462)); RS59/10, 239; 480; 467; RS59/10, 261 (but cf. RS59/9, 29 and 32); 460; 466; 461: 60 ells, but PD119/1/7, p. 119: 66 ells; 465.
23. RS59/12/1, fo. 119.
24. RS59/8, fo. 4659.
25. PD119/1/7, p. 117.
26. Flinn, Michael (ed.): "Scottish population history from the 17th century to the 1930s" (1977), pp. 164-186.
27. A.P. S., vol. XI (1824), pp. 163-167.
28. Smith, J. G.: *ibid.*, p. 188.
29. RS59/10, fo. 168; RS59/9, 29 and 32; RS59/10, 163; *ibid.*, 252.
30. PD119/1/7, pp. 96-113.
31. *Ibid.*, pp. 94-96.
32. RS59/12/1. fo. 119.
33. RS59/9, fo. 29.
34. RS59/11. fo. 95; RS59/12/1, 119.
35. Mitchell, Sir Arthur (ed.): "Geographical Collections relating to Scotland made by Walter Macfarlane" (1906), vol. I, p. 339.
36. S.R.O.: GD24/1/786.
37. To the 23 feus mentioned above have to be added three half-lots split off from existing feus in 1709-1710: RS59/12/2, fos. 450, 476 and 478.
38. British Library: K.TOP XLVIII SH. 25 A-G: sheet 15/4.
39. Stobie, James: Map of the Counties of Perth and Clackmannan (1783): C.R.A.: MP/PC/1; Tait, Rev. Christopher: "Parish of Kincardine", in Old Statistical Account (1791-92, reprinted 1977, vol. XII), p. 551.

Grateful acknowledgement is made to the Keeper of the Records of Scotland for permission to quote from registers of sasines and to Central Regional Council Archives Services for access to PD119.

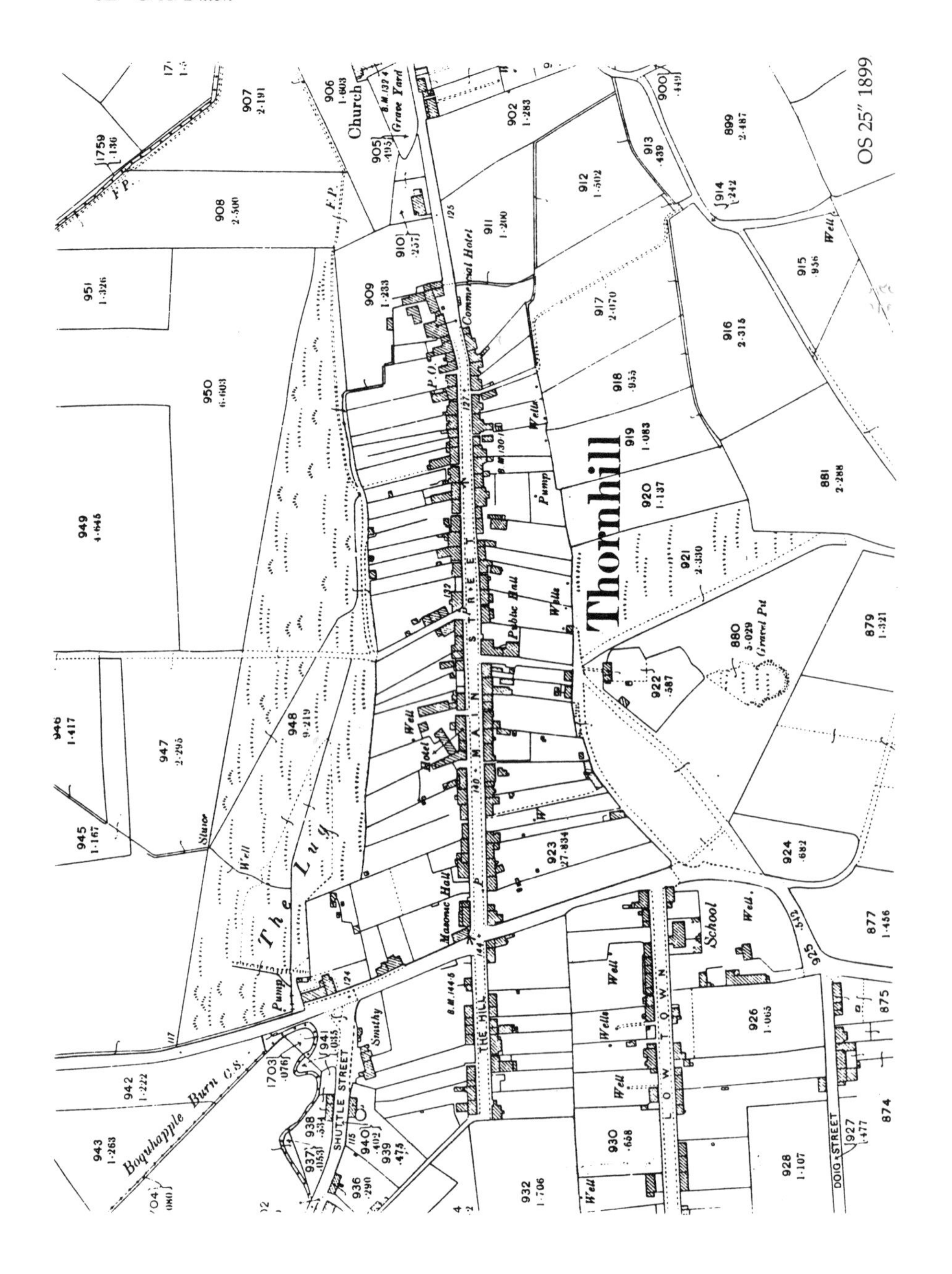
OS 25" 1899
Thornhill
MAIN STREET
THE HILL
LOWTOWN
SHUTTLE STREET
DOIG STREET
The Lug
Church
Grave Yard
Commercial Hotel
P.O.
Public Hall
Masonic Hall
Hotel
School
Smithy
Pump
Well
Wells
Sluice
Gravel Pit
Boquhapple Burn
F.P.

JOSEPH DENOVAN ADAM (1842 - 1896) ANIMAL PAINTER
People Of The Forth (8)

Maria Devaney
Smith Art Gallery & Museum

"Beasts in Bond Street! Sheep in the Salon! Messrs Dowdeswells have taken the wind out of the sails of the Agricultural Hall, and Mr Denovan Adam has given us the opportunity of seeing a superb collection of Scottish Highland Cattle. Mountain, Meadow, Moss and Moor have all been laid under contribution. The result is we can have the chance of studying these hornymental animals without being tossed, and staring at them without being gored."

Punch, November 8th 1890

This review of an exhibition demonstrates the enormous popularity and success enjoyed by Joseph Denovan Adam (Figure 1) as a painter in his life-time. Now however, similarly with many other accomplished artists of the Victorian period, his works are often hidden away in museum stores or dispersed throughout private collections unrecorded and inaccessible to the public eye.

The Smith Art Gallery and Museum in Stirling, which owns five works by the artist is again seeking to bring him back into the limelight by a 1996 exhibition to mark the centenary of his death. The artists of Craigmill and Cambuskenneth including Denovan Adam have been featured locally before e.g. Morley (5) in 1933 and the Smith exhibition of 1978 (1). Following a period of research and public appeals, the Smith has now located a number of paintings held in public and private collections in Scotland and found information in archives in Stirling, Edinburgh and Glasgow to contribute to a new exhibition, 27 April to 1 September 1996.

The son of Joseph Adam and Annie Denovan was born in Glasgow in 1842. His father, a landscape artist active in the period 1858 - 1880, was a major influence and tutor of the young Joseph. Early in Joseph's life the family moved to London to help further his father's career enabling him to submit works to the Royal Academy exhibitions.

THE YOUNG ARTIST

Joseph studied at both South Kensington art school (now the Royal College of Art) and The Royal Academy. Training at the Royal Academy at the time involved copying Old Masters before progressing to sketch from casts, still lifes and then live models in the specially designed studio with its throne and horseshoe of seats. These methods may have influenced his own curriculum years later for his students at Craigmill. Joseph and his father regularly toured

Scotland on sketching holidays, resulting in a number of romantic Highland landscape paintings. This romantic style had been popularised by the Scottish artists Horatio McCulloch (1805 - 67) and Arthur Perigal (1816 - 84). Joseph is also known to have worked jointly on paintings with both his father and Edmund John Niemann (1813 - 1876), a London based artist of part German descent whose works illustrate the varying moods of nature's seasons, which was to become an important theme in Joseph's later work.

These early influences led Joseph to concentrate on landscape and still life. His specific interest in depicting Highland cattle which was to dominate his later work and teaching, although evident at this early stage was not fully developed.

In pursuit of perfecting the subject of Highland cattle he moved permanently back to Scotland in 1872, living initially at Coldwell Villa in Crieff, then from 1874 - 1886/7 at various addresses in Edinburgh. He is known to have attended classes at the art schools in Edinburgh and Glasgow, but no details of his studies there have been located.

Sometime during this period he married Mary Waters Laurie, elder daughter of Thomas Laurie, a painter and fine art dealer of St Vincent Street, Glasgow. A father - in - law in the business of selling paintings would have been a useful ambassador for a struggling artist seeking to establish a reputation. His first wife bore him two daughters, Janet and Mary.

The earliest record of any paintings submitted to public exhibitions is in 1860 with the Royal Academy in London when he was still living with his parents. These early works are recorded as being 'Fruit' and 'Still Lifes'. It was not until the 1870's that Highland landscapes and cattle became his favourite subject.

He continued to submit works to the annual exhibitions of the Royal Academy, Royal Glasgow Institute of the Fine Arts, the Royal Scottish Society of Painters in Watercolours and the Royal Scottish Academy throughout the rest of his life. The sales ledgers of the RSA and the RGI (17) show that he frequently sold well, with prices for his paintings starting at £10-£20 in the early 1870s rising to £500 by the 1890s.

CRAIGMILL

In 1887, Joseph Denovan Adam moved to Stirling with his second wife Annie Lochhead and his children, and there leased Craigmill House (Figure 2) situated on the coaching road from Stirling to Alloa in the hamlet of Craigmill, formerly notorious for the smuggling of whisky (13). For a Highland landscape and animal painter, this quiet rural area offered everything he might need; the Ochils and the Trossachs could provide dramatic landscape backgrounds, and livestock hired from neighbouring farms could act as models. The proximity of Stirling to Glasgow and Edinburgh and its good railway links also enabled Joseph to keep in touch with artistic circles and to submit to annual exhibitions.

The building of the field studio and a series of animal pens in the park opposite Craigmill House to allow the sketching and painting of the animals in their natural habitats in all weathers, was principally designed for his own use. Realising that other artists and students might benefit from these facilities, Joseph developed his field studio into a 'Country Atelier' (Figure 3). Advertisements were placed in magazines e.g. *The Years Art* (22), *Art Review, The Lady*. Each season began on 1st April, and students were offered Animal Drawing, Painting and Anatomy, with emphasis on the study of animal life in natural surroundings and in relationship to landscape.

ADAM'S ATELIER

The establishment of the Country Atelier was the first experiment of its kind in Scotland, and it offered a "stimulus to seek after noble ideals and the pure interpretation of Nature's simplicity" (19). The vogue for outdoor 'naturalism' in painting in the early 1880's to which many British artists were attracted was principally due to the influence of the French artist Jules Bastien-Lepage (1848-84). His 'plein - air' pictures of peasant genre scenes were of high finish and meticulous square brush technique and artists in Scotland and England had generous exposure to his works which were exhibited in Glasgow and London. The popularity of this outdoor realism led to the formation of artists colonies in rural areas, for example in Cockburnspath a circle gathered around Sir James Guthrie (1859-1950) and in Kirkcudbright a group from the Glasgow School, among them Edward Atkinson Hornel (1864-1933). Joseph was a member of such an artistic community which had settled around Stirling and Cambuskenneth. The peaceful riverbanks, old cottages, ancient castle and abbey attracted artists to the area during the summer months, some such as 'Glasgow Boys' William Kennedy settled there permanently. The Craigmill art school became a meeting place for local and visiting artists, providing an atmosphere conducive to experimentation and innovation. It attracted students from different parts of the UK and even from abroad, and established Stirling as a centre of art throughout the late 1880s and 1890s. John MacWhirter R.A. (1839 - 1911) and John Smart R.S.A. (1839 - 1899) were occasional visitors to the studio, but perhaps Joseph's best known pupil was Edith Holden, known as 'The Edwardian Lady' today. She came to Craigmill in 1891 at the age of 20 on the recommendation of her teacher at the Birmingham Municipal Art School. She remained for a year, as a residential student living with the family at Craigmill, and under his guidance her work developed considerably. Her time at the atelier is well documented (8).

The art school is described in the *Stirling Journal* of 22 August 1890 as follows:

> "On one side of the road is the house with its pretty garden and private studios, and a field for the 'Highlanders' beyond, and on the other one enters through a gate in the high wall, the park, or, atelier 'en plein air'. Here we find the students at work, some at the mare and foal, some at a pretty group of sheep and lambs, another pupil busy with a goat and its

playful kid, or grouping poultry, of which there is a large choice. Ingenious contrivances have been made for the securing of those sometimes too lively models, but which in no way spoils the open air effect or confines the movement of the animals to their hurt. Picturesque and suitable backgrounds in relation to the groups, are thus obtained, and the work goes on steadily, even though the weather prove unpropitious, for in the middle of the field stands the atelier, built principally of glass, with windows so arranged that on stormy days the students can work from within. Here also are carried on the anatomical studies required for animal painting. A tennis court adjoins, used in 'off hours'."

The establishment of the atelier did much to enhance the reputation of Joseph Denovan Adam whose paintings of Highland cattle were becoming well known through the important exhibitions of the period. Contemporary accounts also indicate the respect and regard his students held for him. His sympathetic yet effective teaching together with his great knowledge of animals helped to launch many promising students on their artistic careers. Joseph took as many as 25 students each year, mostly lodged locally, with a small number accommodated in his own home with his wife and children.

Joseph kept for some years a small herd of Highland Cattle, and since these animals were not usually seen so far south as Stirling, this created much local interest. A contemporary wrote:

"To Highland cattle Denovan Adam's heart turns with especial fondness. He has made them his particular study, and is an authority on breeds and stock ... Over all horned beasts, Mr Adam has almost a magnetic power, he knows no fear of them and will walk up with confidence to the most truculent looking bull ... 'Don't be afraid of them, and you are all right' says Mr Adam." (e.g. picture 'Cattle' on *FNH* 18 cover)

A strict rule for all his students was a thorough grounding in the anatomy of animals, and for this a complete skeleton of a cow decorated the student's studio. An account of the time mentions how the students would groan when he insisted on a correct drawing of all the bones, after which studies of the muscles were drawn from books, with an occasional cattle head from the local butcher to be painted. Only then were students allowed to tackle the various live models in the park, which included a very docile pedigree Highland bull, numerous sheep, horses, goats and different varieties of poultry. Dogs of different breeds, greyhound, bloodhound, Irish wolfhound, collies, spaniels and pug all occasionally provided models.

Joseph himself would paint from memory, and he had a few six foot landscape studies in progress in his own private studio. Occasionally he would invite a few favourite students to see his method of working. Although Joseph's work was always personal and powerful, it was not until his time at Craigmill that it attained a unity of effect without which individuality of conception and vigorous technique alike are ineffective pictorially. He was a prolific and strenuous worker, many of the canvases are of large size, and his vigorous method was best suited for paintings on such a scale. This period at

Craigmill was perhaps the most rewarding both for his career and socially. Contemporary accounts describe its congenial atmosphere, and Joseph is described as a "kind and genial friend, a man of keen sensibilities and gifted talents who exercised a marked influence both in social and artistic circles" (19). His love of the Stirling area is demonstrated in the large number of paintings inspired by it (Figure 4), and he became a valued member of the community. He was leader for many years of Logie Parish Church Choir, with a reputation for always being willing to be `of service', offering his musical talents to good causes.

ACCLAIM

In November 1890 Joseph's reputation as an artist was established in London with his solo exhibition at the Dowdeswells galleries in Bond Street. Ninety-seven paintings were shown and the exhibition was an enormous success, bringing to the attention of both public and art critics the work of Scotland's foremost animal painter. A contemporary writer noted "an avid desire to buy that was manifested by the visitors". The Stirling Reference Library holds a book of reviews of this exhibition (14), only two of the 50 are poor. Some of his best reviews were from *Punch* (op cit), and the *Illustrated London News* (9). The *Sunday Times* critic writes;

> "He is no mere cattle painter who puts in conventional landscapes to serve as scenery for his animal subjects but he paints with realistic truth the cattle he knows intimately, yet with an unerring artistic sense of their true pictorial relation to their surroundings."

This exhibition brought Joseph both commercial success and critical acclaim. Critics compared his work to two other notable animal painters of the period, Rosa Bonheur (1822-1899) and Sir Edwin Landseer (1802-73).

Rosa Bonheur was a French artist who enjoyed great popularity in Britain in the 1850's. She visited the Scottish Highlands which fascinated her. Her animal paintings are free from any sentimentality, and have an authentic honesty. It is said that she dressed as a man in order to visit abattoirs and markets in her search for knowledge.

Sir Edwin Landseer was a great favourite of Queen Victoria's and the general public. His animal subjects tend to be sentimental and as John Ruskin observed "departed from the true nature of the animal for the sake of a pretty thought or a pretty jest".

ROYAL SCOTTISH ACADEMICIAN

Joseph Denovan Adam had achieved public and critical acclaim, had been elected an Associate of the Royal Scottish Academy in 1884, but had to wait until 1892 for the full membership of Academician. The painting `Evening, Strathspey' (oil on canvas, RSA Collection) was exhibited in 1891 at the Royal Scottish Academy, held at that time in the National Gallery of Scotland. In the October of the following year, he offered this painting to the Academy as his

Diploma Work. James L Caw (18) describes this painting as "his masterpiece, and a complete epitome of what he was capable of at his best". The same year he was awarded a gold medal at Munich, and 'Evening, Strathspey' was exhibited in Birmingham in late 1892, early 1893, and then at the Paris Salon in 1894. At this time the French Government offered to purchase the painting, but it had already become the property of the Royal Scottish Academy.

In the Spring of 1895 his popular appeal was further enhanced by a follow up exhibition at the Dowdeswells galleries entitled 'The Months in Scotland', paintings "illustrative of the phases of animal life ... and of the march of the seasons amongst the hills and glens and along the seashores" (18), and commemorated in a limited edition book by R.S. Shearer & Son of Stirling. Joseph Denovan Adam was by then at the height of his powers. A contemporary critic commented:

> "In his early works he appears as a painter simply of cattle, but later the cattle appear in proper relation to their surroundings, in harmony with the mood of weather and conditions of the country... Each beast varies as much from its fellow in expression as the faces in a crowd of human beings" (*The Artist*).

AN ARTISTS PHILOSOPHY

The preface to his earlier exhibition in 1890 suggested his own artistic aims and desires. He placed an emphasis on getting to know his subjects, (i.e. his animals) and their particular characteristics. This is reflected in his early work where the cattle are almost the only point of interest, with the background of less importance. As his work developed and matured, the animals became integrated into their natural habitat, portraying a harmony between beast and nature, reflecting his new strategy in which "the life he paints adds to the poetry of the scenes in which it is found" (18). It is worth considering this important development in his work in the context of innovations being introduced to Scotland by the 'Glasgow Boys' and others. Joseph's own maturing powers, and contact with this younger generation of painters from the Glasgow School when they visited Stirling, seem to have had an effect on his approach to his art. Both his use of colour and brushstrokes become more vigorous and decorative. A further comparison can be drawn with the introduction of cabbages onto the canvas!

'Cattle in Cabbage Field' (oil on canvas, Glasgow Collection), is evocative of Sir James Guthrie's 'A Hind's Daughter' (National Gallery of Scotland collection) painted in 1883, which depicts a young girl in a field of cabbages. A local story tells of George Henry and William Kennedy while visiting the studio of a young artist in Cambuskenneth busily painting a picture of cattle in the orchard, advising him to go outside and paint a cabbage!

Other artists working at the same time as Joseph Denovan Adam included William MacTaggart (1835-1920), who by the 1870's in tandem with Impressionism in France, was painting with a raw freedom of expression born 'of the rush and dash' of painting direct from nature. James MacNeill Whistler (1834-1903) was also painting his series of Nocturnes, and an interesting comparison can be drawn with his use of the butterfly motif, and Joseph's cattle motifs used as a signature on two watercolours in Glasgow's collection. The 1880's saw Post Impressionism in France and the last stages of Pre-Raphaelitism in Britain. It is also possible that Joseph may have seen early work by the Colourist Samuel John Peploe (1871-1935) who attended life class at the Royal Scottish Academy in the 1890's.

AN UNTIMELY DEATH

Leaving Craigmill in 1895, Joseph moved to Callander leasing a house called Balkerach. He occupied it only for a short while as ill health forced him to move to Glasgow (4 Oakvale, University Avenue), possibly to be close to the Western Infirmary. He suffered from Bright's Disease, the degeneration of the kidneys (cirrhosis). He died there on 22 April 1896 at the age of 54.

He was reported to have borne his suffering bravely and to the last maintained the pleasant humour for which he was noted. He had been much esteemed by a very wide circle reflected by the large attendance at his funeral. Obituary notices mention the 'magnificent wreaths of flowers' which almost hid the casket at the burial service in Cathcart Cemetery. Many Glasgow artists attended including John Smart R.S.A., and J. Henderson R.S.A., the Presidents of both the Royal Scottish Academy and the Glasgow Art Club. The service itself was conducted by the parish minister of Logie.

He was survived by a widow and seven children, two from his first marriage. A will of 1886 set up a trust - income for his wife during her lifetime on the understanding that she didn't remarry, and that she maintained their five children until they reached their majority. (The other two children were provided for by their grandfather, father of Adam's first wife).

Joseph's finished paintings were sold at a public auction, which grossed £3,718. Those not reaching value were held back for future sales, some being exhibited posthumously at the Royal Scottish Academy and elsewhere. His final estate totalled £5,071.48, equivalent of a quarter of a million pounds today. His widow lived for a time at Belmont Gardens, Hillhead, and in 1906 returned to Callander to rooms in a boarding house, Inverteith. She was to move residence in Callander twice more before she died in 1942 when the Trust was finally wound up.

Of his children, Janet married John Roberts, an artist, and lived at Balhaldie House in Dunblane, before moving to Drummond Lodge in Callander, close to Balkerach. Her sister Mary lived with them. Annie married in 1909 and became a Mrs Rose of New Barnet, Hertfordshire. Joseph Denovan Adam junior followed in his father's footsteps and became an artist in Glasgow, exhibiting between 1920-30 at the Royal Scottish Academy. John Lochhead Adam, a ship surveyor, lived latterly in Mugdock, Milngavie. The other two sons James and McDonald emigrated to Saskatchewan, Canada in 1906.

LOCATING THE PAINTINGS

Tracing the life story of any painting is a time consuming task demanding the skills of a private detective. To attempt to document the whereabouts of the entire output of one artist dating back over a hundred years is virtually impossible, given that titles of pictures often change, and pictures in private hands are rarely accessed through public archives.

Taking the paintings by Joseph Denovan Adam now held in public collections, examining their histories may provide some clues as to the fate of his canvases. Of such so far located only two were purchased, `Balmoral-Autumn' (Oil on Canvas, 1896, Glasgow Collection) and `Highland Cattle' (oil on canvas, Paisley Collection). All others seem to have been gifted from private collections, indicating the mass popularity of Adam's work with the picture buying public in his lifetime, and for a time after.

Taste and fashions change, and at some point Joseph Denovan Adam fell from favour. His pictures have rarely been displayed or published, except for auctions, where much of his output is to be found. Over a hundred of his paintings have passed through auction sales since 1973, with pictures appearing in Scotland, England, Canada, USA, Germany, Austria, the Netherlands, South Africa and Sweden. Even works in public collections, although not fully explored to date, seem to be equally scattered, appearing in Scotland, Northern Ireland, Latvia and New Zealand.

To conclude, perhaps it would be fitting to reiterate these verses from the obituary in the *Stirling Journal* (1 May 1896), which summarize the artist's contribution to posterity. It was just signed 'x'.

"Nature hath claimed him - he hath pass'd from here
Who gave to nature all his heart and life,
And sought her ceaselessly thro' toil and strife,
To yield the secrets that she held most dear;
Nor sought in vain: and tho' above his bier
We bow the head while eyes with tears are rife
For desolate children and for widowed wife,
Yet mourn we less for him, nor harbour fear
That Fame shall let him die; for in his work
Lives he not still? - a presence strongly felt
Speaking from out each canvas, that shall lurk
Long in the favour'd land wherein he dwelt.
And yet must Friendship grieve that Death outran
So great an artist and so true a man!

No more his genial presence shall be seen,
Or felt within his hospitable door
No more shall shaggy herd on hill or moor
Own his depicting skill: the shifting sheen
Of the revolving seasons - Springtide green,
Summer or Autumn, Winter's snow clad floor-

His hand shall not interpret as of yore,
Since now alas, 'tis fled from things terrene!
So short is life!' What genius can delay,
What art protect the length of Nature's term!
But yet his influence cannot pass away,
For built on Truth is its foundation firm.
A life well spent, high purpose well fulfill'd,
Now comes the well-earned rest that Heaven hath will'd"

ACKNOWLEDGEMENTS

Research - Evelyn Paton. Additional Research - Elma Lindsay. Also to:

Sharon Briggs, Art Sales Index; Melva Croal, Manchester City Art Galleries; George Dixon, Central Regional Archives; Anne Escott, The Mitchell Library, Glasgow; J.D. Fordyce, Eastwood District Council; Roger Frame, Royal Scottish Society of Painters in Watercolours; Susan Gideon; Barbara Hilton-Smith, Witt Library, Courtauld Institute; A.M. Jackson, Strathclyde Regional Archives; Helen Kennett; Bob McCutcheon, The Bookshop, Spittal Street, Stirling; A.W. Potter, Royal Academy of Arts; Joanna Soden, Royal Scottish Academy; Diane Spaul, Victoria & Albert Museum; Martin Tyson, Scottish Record Office, and lenders to the exhibition.

REFERENCES, SOURCES, FURTHER READING

1. The Artists of Craigmill and Cambuskenneth 1880 - 1920, James K. Thomson, Smith Art Gallery and Museum, 1978.
2. Calendar of Confirmations of Testaments, 1896.
3. Catalogue of Glasgow Art Gallery and Museum, Kelvingrove, 1908.
4. A Concise History of English Painting, William Gaunt.
5. Craigmill Art School and Cambuskenneth Painters. Henry Morley. *Stirling Field and Archaeological Society Transactions* 56 (1933) 38-46.
6. Dictionary of Scottish Art & Architecture, Peter J.M. McEwan.
7. Dictionary of Scottish Painters 1600 - 1960, Paul Harris and Julian Halsby.
8. The Edwardian Lady – The Story of Edith Holden, Ina Taylor, M. Joseph, 1980.
9. *The Illustrated London News*, 8 November 1890.
10. Letters of Joseph Denovan Adam to Royal Scottish Academy 1884-1894.
11. *The Magazine of Art*, December 1887.
12. *Oban Times* 2 May 1896.
13. Ordnance Gazetteer of Scotland, Francis Groome (Editor).
14. Press Notices of an Exhibition of Highland Cattle, November 1890.
15. Royal Scottish Academy Exhibitions 1826-1990, Hilmarton Press, 1991.
16. Royal Scottish Academy Notes, 1878, 1881, Annual Report, 1896.
17. Sales Ledgers 1870-1882, Royal Glasgow Institute.
18. Scottish Painting Past and Present 1620-1908, J. L. Caw, Jack, Edinburgh, 1908.
19. *Stirling Journal & Advertiser* 22 August and 14 November 1890, 1 May 1896.
20. *Stirling Observer* 29 April 1896.
21. Will and Sederunt Book of Joseph Denovan Adam.
22. *The Year's Art* 1893, 1894 Boussod, Baladon & Co, London.

Figure 1 Joseph Denovan Adam. Smith

See also cover photograph 'Cattle 1887'.

Figure 3 Interior of the Atelier (studio) Craigmill. Sketch by M. F. Struthers c1900. Smith

Figure 2 Craigmill House, with remainder of the original larger atelier. Smith

Figure 4 Ploughing in the Carse of Stirling. Adam

CLAN GREGOR AND ITS SETTLEMENT IN RANNOCH: A REVIEW OF TRADITIONAL SOURCES

Sheila McGregor

The ghosts of Clan Gregor today share the empty lands of Rannoch with the ghosts of many other tribes - Robertsons, Campbells, Menzies, Camerons, even a few MacDonalds - but, if their own stories are to be believed, the Gregorach[1] are perhaps the oldest and most tenacious of all. Their later history is more or less documented, but, in addition, four versions of their settlement tradition were transcribed from oral sources c1800 and are considered here. Similar traditions are hinted at for other people in other parts of Scotland but do not seem to have survived in quite such detail. As ethnological documents these four versions appear to be of considerable interest.

It is not entirely surprising that such traditions should have survived in Rannoch when they have been almost entirely lost elsewhere, even in Perthshire. Its remoteness from centralised authority and material civilisation allowed and indeed required the old ways of life to continue. Even in earlier days, when few people had any reason to travel faster than their herd of cattle, Rannoch was remote, and seems to have been one of the last areas into which the Gregorach, or MacGregors, moved. It was at the extreme north-west edge of the Clan lands, which once stretched (according to various traditions) from Lorne in Argyll through Glen Dochart and Breadalbane as far as Kenmore, and from Rannoch to Comrie, the Trossachs, the Lennox and Loch Lomond. For a very long time, in its primitive way, Rannoch supported a substantial, self-contained and self-sustaining community, with a confident and utterly Gaelic culture of considerable interest.

This self-sufficient culture seems to have been more or less intact when it was suddenly exposed in the second part of the eighteenth century to the critical scrutiny of the Commissioners of the Forfeited Estates (SHS 1909), a body of competent, middle-class, Edinburgh, civil servants, who had become responsible for the administration of the Rannoch estate of Robertson of Strowan, held by his family for over four hundred years but forfeited to the Crown after the events of 1745-6. At this late date, its inhabitants were still producing only enough to live on and cover their landlord's modest expenses, what might be termed a sufficiency economy, but, for all the apparent poverty, the level of exploitation was sustainable. One of the priorities of the Commissioners was to change this state of affairs by teaching the natives how to increase their productivity in various ways, in order that a cash surplus could be raised to be spent on such modern facilities as schools, housing and public health. The Commissioners enclosed the arable, improved roads, built bridges, planted trees, killed foxes and eagles, installed teachers, and provided such mixed modern blessings as small-pox vaccination, spinning wheels, looms and religious education. Thus was the modern age brought to Rannoch and the process initiated of rapid emigration over the new bridges and down the new roads to places with even more modern facilities, a process which has continued to the present day and led to the extinction of the native community. According to their own story, which will be studied below, the tribal community in Rannoch had a continuous history, from their first land-taking, of more than two thousand years, which is by no means impossible to accept in such a conservative area and which can be paralleled elsewhere in Scotland. Given the marked stability of the old system throughout this long period, and the numbers supported by the area then, in contrast to its present tax-funded desolation, it is possible to think that this corner of Scotland has been singularly unfortunate in its encounter with progress.

Traditional accounts

Four traditional accounts survive of the settlement by Clan Gregor, on the north side of Loch Rannoch and westwards towards Rannoch Moor, in one of the most remote parts of the Scottish mainland. All show adaptation to later historical conventions but all contain elements of an original story which is by no means conventional. The main source (Murray MacGregor) is Amelia Murray MacGregor's *History of the Clan Gregor*, published in two volumes in 1898 and 1901, which contains valuable transcriptions of original documents. The purpose of the stories is not purely entertainment. Clan Gregor regarded itself as entitled to occupy its lands in Rannoch by tribal law, and the stories in fact present the legal argument by which they attempted to justify their continued presence there through many attempts to remove them.

1. **From a memoir by Lieut. Alexander MacGregor in Innerhaddon, c1800 (Murray MacGregor 1901, 216).**
   "It is universally admitted by the oldest MacGregors in Rannoch in their traditional histories that the Family of Ardlarich is no other than the identical family of MacGregor, although it is not easy at this remote period to ascertain with any degree of certainty when or how they got possession there. It is however affirmed by tradition that a succession of the Lairds or Chiefs of MacGregor lived in Ardlarich, [and that one of them] founded the Island of Loch Rannoch which is a collection, or immense cairn, of loose stones laid upon cross rafters of wood joined together. This island was built at immense trouble and expense for the purpose of building a storehouse thereon where to deposit his most valuable effects during times of trouble."

This description of the method by which crannogs were constructed reveals knowledge of a process which was not otherwise described, or generally understood, before the draining of the Eaderloch, at the north end of Loch Treig, in 1941, which revealed its layered construction[2]. Is it possible that this formidable undertaking, which would have involved the whole community for many weeks and possibly over months and years, was remembered over two thousand years? I can see no other satisfactory explanation for this very specific and accurate description early in the nineteenth century. The Isle of

Loch Rannoch is still undated, but may have been built as early as c500 BC, shortly after the crannogs of Loch Tay[3], though the land-taking and sub-division may have been of earlier date. The use in the construction of the Loch Tay crannogs of timbers of standard size, noted in the excavations there, suggests a considerable period of planning (at least a century) before construction began (I am indebted to Dr T N Dixon for this observation).

2. **A translation from the Gaelic account of 'an old Rannoch man' given to John Robertson, Old Blair, c1800 (Murray MacGregor 1901, 477).**
"The Laird of Roro in Glenlyon had three sons, and to the eldest he gave forty cows with their followers and said, 'You have now come to man's estate. This is your portion and you must go forth and find grass and holding for yourself.' He set his face north-westwards, and camped for a time on a hill-side in the Struan estate called *Leacainn na bo gile*. About this time a party of Stewarts from Appin had been on an excursion towards Perth, and returned by way of Rannoch. At Dunan, about three miles beyond the head of Loch Rannoch, and on the left or north bank of the water of Gaur, there dwelt at this time a sept or tribe (of Stewarts, I think) called *Clann I'n Bhuidhe*[3a], whom the Appin men came athwart on their way, and from whom they received scant hospitality and rough handling; but they held their way westward, and camped about the side of Loch Luidan, in no grateful mood towards *Clann I'n Bhuidhe*. Here the leader espied the encampment on the south side of the wide valley, on *Leacainn na bo gile*, and he sent a man or two across to ask passing hospitality, in the hope of meeting with the customary courtesy extended to civil strangers. They reached MacGregor's camp and told their tale, and he gave them not only bread, but sent one of his beeves as a present to their leader. On the return of the party, Stewart questioned his men, and on getting their report he said, 'This is no ordinary man. He has given us not only ordinary hospitality, but has sent a generous present. I must go and see him and thank him in person.' And across the moor with a few attendants Stewart made his way to MacGregor's camp. MacGregor received him courteously and informed him that he was only camping there for a while with a view to move on in search of suitable grazing whereon to settle with his men and cattle. Says Stewart, 'We have passed through very fine grazing ground between this and Loch Rannoch, which is now held by a bad race called *Clann I'n Bhuidhe*. They treated us very badly on our way westward, but we were few in number and unable to cope with them, but your party and mine combined would more than match them; and as you have dealt so handsomely by us, we shall be glad to go back with you to Dunan. We shall not leave a man alive of Clann I'n Bhuidhe (*cha'n fhag sinn ceann air amhaich dhuibh*) and at Dunan you and yours shall settle.' Combine the two parties did, and they were as good as their word in dealing with Clann I'n Bhuidhe. A bloody fight took place at a burn near Dunan called to this day *Caochan-na-fola*[4]. Not a man of Clann I'n Bhuidhe was left alive, and MacGregor settled at Dunan, and there founded the first of the three MacGregor 'Houses' in Rannoch. He prospered at Dunan, and in no long

> time his two younger brothers followed him from Glenlyon to Rannoch, and he succeeded in settling the one at Ardlarich and the other at Lerigan, and these became the other MacGregor 'Houses' in Rannoch, thus possessing among them the whole north side or *Slios Min* of Loch Rannoch.
>
> A considerable time after the eldest MacGregor had settled at Dunan he had gone to a great hunting to Dùn Seilg, in Argyle. At this hunt two hounds of MacGregor's surpassed all the other hounds so much that the Chief of Argyle made particular enquiry, and said, 'The owner of such dogs as these must be a man of mark. Who is he? I should wish to see him.' The reply was, 'The owner of the hounds is MacGregor of Dunan in Rannoch,' and straighway *Fear Dhunan* was introduced to Argyle. After some conversation, Argyle asked him on what tenure he held his lands. 'On *this* tenure,' said MacGregor, touching his sword. Said Argyle, 'That tenure is good, and good enough at present; but, mark my words, the day is coming and is not far distant, when *that* will not suffice you. The law is day by day drawing nearer to us, and the man who cannot shew *coir righ* (king's title) for his lands will assuredly lose them: and, as I should wish to befriend you, I will, if you wish it, apply to the King and obtain for you a lawful title to your possessions.' MacGregor thanked him warmly, but said that he was quite contented with his rights as they stood, and that he would make them good against all comers; and he and his hounds returned to Dunan.
>
> Menzies of Weem ('The Menzies were always wise in their generation,' says MacGregor!) knew the wild but good grazing district of Rannoch and knew also that the MacGregors had no *written* rights to their holdings there; so to Scone he hied and easily got from the King a title to this outlying and little known wilderness. In due time he established a settlement at *Cinnachlachair*, near where Rannoch Lodge now stands, and asserted his legal rights against the MacGregors, but little cared they for a time for him and his 'writings' and they held their own, at the very least, against him, until at last, wearied and worried, he consulted a leading man of his own clan in Appin of Dull called the 'Crowner' as to the expediency of maintaining his fruitless fight with the MacGregors. 'Hold your ground,' says the Crowner. 'They may harrass you for some time yet, but the law is daily becoming stronger, and if you persevere, you will wear them out through time.' This worldly-wise advice was followed and prevailed, and the Menzieses held and still hold their ground in Rannoch."

The introduction of the Stewart interest, and similar details, vary from one version to another and are clearly attempts to explain and justify aspects of the original story that must have puzzled later generations as the story was told and retold over many centuries. Such rationalisations are a very common feature of old folk-tales brought up to date. In particular, the story-teller would need to justify the extermination of Clan Iain Bhuidhe, which appears to be an original feature, and the taking of their land, which he could do in terms of Stewart landlords, or kings, since, perhaps as far back as the memory of story-tellers in Rannoch could go, land had been allocated by Stewarts. His suggestion here, which is unique to this version, that Clan Iain Bhuidhe may themselves have been Stewarts, would add to the authority of the Stewart of the story over them. The historical facts of Clan Gregor settlement in Rannoch of course run contrary to the theme of these tales, since the Clan in Rannoch had no permission from any Stewart to settle there - if they had, the rest of the story would not have happened as it did, and these stories would not have survived.

The involvement of the Menzieses with Rannoch was at a period much later than the original settlement and the mention of their tribal 'Crowner' may add one more to the total of Perthshire Tossachdereths or land judges. At one time this office was filled by John Meyners or Menzies, who was established at Kingallin, north of Drummond Hill, in the Abthanerie of Dull[5]. These powerful officials were not uncommon in tribal Perthshire, and appear to have been established under various landlords at Morenish and Ardtalnaig on Loch Tay[6], at Roro in Glen Lyon[7], at Tulliemet in Strathtay[8], and at Monzievaird in Strathearn[9].

The story of the migration to Rannoch may be placed convincingly on the modern map; indeed, *Leacan na bo Gile* still exists, and may well have some such genuine history attached to it. There is of course an element of *bòilich*, or boasting, without which no story in the bardic tradition would be complete. But the first part of the story of the settlement is original and unexplained and bears no relationship to anything known in historical times in Western Europe, though it is familiar to us from hundreds of folk tales of less specific interest, in which all the sons leave home to seek their fortune, the eldest first. The implication is that they leave their sister behind on the family farm, which she inherits in due course. In other words, this describes a matrilineal inheritance system, of which traces have survived in many parts of Europe, and which was used by the Picts up to the ninth century AD (for which we have the evidence of various historical sources[10]). One may imagine the pastoral farmers of the Neolithic moving slowly across the landscape, generation by generation, in just this fashion. It is not explained where, eventually, they were to find their wives, but new land-taking was evidently not an every-day event. The emphasis on good grazing is striking.

3. **A traditional version of the Rannoch family history (summarised in Murray MacGregor 1901, 215-6).**
   The first MacGregor of Ardlarich was an illegitimate son of the Laird of MacGregor and about the thirteenth century, assisted by Duncan Robertson of Strowan in this instance, 'he banished from the north side of Loch Rannoch a tribe called Clann an Lea, who were in the Baliol interest.'

A different historical background has here been stitched on to the older story of settlement in Rannoch, equally in response to a need to make the story of land-taking credible to the audience of the day. In this version, as in others, the Stewart interest is implicated, and the support of the Robertsons acknowledged. The story of illegitimate descent from the Chief appears to be an attempt to explain the ambiguous link between Ardlarich and the main line of the Clan, a link which was known and accepted within the Clan but no longer understood

4. **Kenneth MacLeay, *Historical Memoirs* of Rob Roy and the Clan MacGregor (1818, 66).**
"It was at a very remote period that the district of Rannach became the property of the Macgregors; and that in a manner which shews the barbarous character of the age. It chanced that the then laird of Appin, whose name was Stewart, a branch of the primeval lords of Lochawe, was travelling with his lady and their usual retinue of walking attendants, from the city of Perth to their property in Argyllshire. In passing through Rannach they were interrupted and plundered of their baggage, and otherwise maltreated, by a certain tribe of the natives, now only known by the patronymic of *Clan-ic-Jan-bhui*, the grand-children of yellow John. In order to revenge this injury, Stewart collected a body of vassals, and marched with them to Rannach. On his way, at Loch Tuille, a small lake at the head of Glenurchy, near the present road through Glenco, he was joined by a son of the chief of Macgregor, who resided in a castle on a small island in that lake. The devoted clan of *ic-Jan-bhui*, with their wives, their children, and their kindred, were cruelly put to the sword; and Stewart, in return for the services rendered him by Macgregor, placed him in the possessions of the exterminated race, where he remained, and was the founder of a new family, which afterwards became chief of the name."

Kenneth MacLeay's compilation of traditional sources, *Historical Memoirs of Rob Roy and the Clan MacGregor* was written at the height of Romanticism, and suffers from the lack of strict historical objectivity typical of the age. His book is generally regarded as semi-fiction, giving a distorted view of the native history of the Highlands. However, this account, which appears to have been taken down from an oral source shortly before 1818, is very similar to that recorded from the old man of Rannoch by Robertson of Blair c1800, which suggests that the embellishments and rationalisations are probably in the original, and derive more from the desire of the native story-teller to create an impressive story than in rewriting by MacLeay for the same purpose. The claim to the chiefship is an old one and repeated in several contexts, but does not concern us here, except insofar as it emphasises the belief held by the Rannoch branch of the Clan, that they were as old as any other surviving branch, though perhaps in some manner junior to them. The involvement of the Stewarts of Appin is a little difficult to explain, but the only justification for the varied historical fictions introduced (such as Clann an Lea being in the Balliol interest) is that they add some authority to the land-taking, which, of course, was not blessed by a royal charter.

There are some new details of considerable interest. The involvement of a family of Gregorach living on the crannog on Loch Tulla is a new element, and may represent some genuine recollection of a related family established there (probably c 500 BC) who were part of the same land-taking to the north and west of Glen Lyon. Loch Tulla is adjacent to Glenorchy and to Achallader, an ancient and very strategic site in this area which was first occupied by Fletchers, traditionally the first people to light fire and boil water in Glenurchy, and so its aboriginal inhabitants. Like most of the natives, they were removed by Campbells expanding steadily from Loch Awe.

Crannogs and Clan Gregor

The mention of two crannogs, or man-made islands, in these stories is probably not a coincidence. In several other contexts, which will be explored below, there are hints or traditions which associate Clan Gregor with specific crannogs or with areas where there are particular concentrations of them[11]. This does not prove that they built them, of course, but some ancestral connection seems a valid hypothesis, though they seem to have possessed, well into the Middle Ages, a value which would now be unsuspected, which ensured that those of Loch Tay, for example, passed through many hands before being finally abandoned. Certainly they remained in regular use over a very long period. The dates for those excavated in Loch Tay suggest a date of construction of 600 BC or thereabouts, and the survival of these islands above water-level depends on regular maintenance.

The account of the building of the Isle of Loch Rannoch is the only known traditional story which attributes the building of a specific crannog to a specific family. If this were an isolated point, it might be unimportant, but in context it adds significant weight to an argument that sees Clan Gregor as, in some sense, the descendants of the original pastoral farmers, who divided up the land for transhumance farming and gave Perthshire essentially its modern shape perhaps as long as three thousand years ago. This, of course, is purely a theory, but it is a theory which fits all the known facts, and which explains many otherwise puzzling aspects of local history, not least, the bitter persecution of Clan Gregor from the sixteenth century onwards.

This kind of man-made island is known in many Scottish waters, from Shetland to Galloway, but is perhaps most numerous in the inland lochs of central Perthshire and adjacent parts of Argyll, where more than fifty have now been identified, and as many more may remain to be found. Surface remains of crannogs may still be seen in Loch Tay, Loch Rannoch, Loch Tulla, Loch Earn, and Loch Voil, of which the last four have Clan Gregor associations. Those on Loch Rannoch and on Loch Tulla have already been mentioned. The Isle of Loch Rannoch is in the very centre of the Loch near its western end, almost invisible from the shore when the weather is rough, a tiny dot on which some kind of stone structure can be made out. Instead of being conveniently close to the shore, it perches precariously near the edge of the sharp drop found in most Scottish lochs, where the trough gouged out by glaciation plunges sharply downwards, perhaps indeed, as claimed by tradition, a rare example of an island constructed purely for defensive purposes, but, equally possibly, a staging post for cattle or small boats attempting to cross the loch. The crannog on Loch Tulla was said by MacLeay (in the context of the

Rannoch oral history copied above) to have been the home of a chief of Clan Gregor at a period before the building of the Isle of Loch Rannoch.

Other associations with Clan Gregor may be claimed for Neish's Island, the crannog at the east end of Loch Earn, since the Neishes claim Clan Gregor affiliation, and for MacGregor's Island, in Loch Voil but now attached to the mainland near Stronvar, in Balquhidder. It was the home of Iain Glass, a leading member of the Clan and a local landowner, until he was killed at the Rout of Glenfruin in 1602. Subsequently, the island was used by 'outlaws' - Lady Grange was held there on her way to distant exile, in 1732, and then abandoned[12]. In view of the date, which was two years before Rob Roy died, the 'outlaws' were almost certainly Macgregors of the Clan Dougal Ciar. Recently a third crannog was found in Loch Voil near the former MacGregor township of Craigruie. One may predict that many more remain to be found[13], notably in Loch Voil, in Loch Earn, in Loch Rannoch and in Loch Tummel, wherever suitable underwater conditions are matched by suitable farmland on shore. The pattern found in Loch Tay suggests that there might be one crannog for every early township site (Morrison 1985, 79), with a few extra ones for purposes which remain speculative but appear to have been communal, and such purposes as hospitality for travellers, and staging posts in the swimming of cattle across lochs have been suggested.

A more general association of crannogs with Clan Gregor may be argued. Lochtayside was traditionally Clan Gregor territory - 'our wash-basin' as one chief is said to have described it - but by the twelfth century, it was royal property, and its crannogs had apparently been neglected, though they were not beyond repair. This period of Perthshire history is obscure but the collapse of the matrilineal Pictish system after AD 900 or so may have led to an upsurge in the use of armed conflict to decide land ownership, which is a feature of patrilineal systems, and which might have led to a prolonged period of disruption in the former Pictish territories, including Atholl. The crannogs, however, cannot have been neglected for very long, as twenty-four, probably the entire prehistoric total, survived sufficiently well to be rebuilt by Alexander I in Loch Tay (Gillies 1938, 35). Nineteen of these have so far been identified by underwater surveys carried out in the 1980s (Morrison 1985), and all those so far dated were built c600 BC.

The extent of rebuilding has not yet been identified by dating. If there had been subsidence, which was a common occurrence, the top level could be raised above the level of the water by adding another layer or two of wooden rafts covered with loose stones - a continuation, essentially, of the basic construction method. This could sufficiently explain how knowledge of the underlying technique survived locally, as we saw in the memoir supplied by Lieut. Alexander MacGregor (1 above). Normally, annual maintenance was restricted to piling on boatloads of stones of medium size, which give these little watery refuges their typically stony or pebbly appearance. Stones also had to be deposited around them, especially on the windward side, to protect the timbers against erosion and the fabric from being washed away during storms.

Some had stone breakwaters to protect them. Without regular maintenance of this kind, crannogs disappear from the surface, as the timbers above the waterline rot away, and most today are reduced to the appearance of underwater cairns, great piles of stones massed up on a sandy or muddy bottom.

Among the crannogs rebuilt by Alexander I was the Isle of Loch Tay, a very large island which is perhaps partly natural, where his Queen, Sybilla, died and was buried in 1122 and on which a priory was subsequently built in her memory. Other crannogs are specifically mentioned in later charters and were retained for such uses as orchards, or kennels, well into the late Middle Ages (Gillies 1938, 34-40). Throughout this period, Clan Gregor occupied lands to north, south and west of Loch Tay, though without royal sanction.

A similar tradition of even more remote times links Clan Gregor with Loch Awe, which has at least twenty crannogs (Morrison 1985, 85). 'The Lion of Loch Awe' was an honorific title of the chief of the Glenstrae branch, and at least three 'homesteads', or cattle pens at the north end of Loch Awe served the network of routes linking Loch Awe to the 'three glens' of Glen Strae, Glenorchy and Glen Lochy, west through the Pass of Brander to the sea, and east to Strathfillan and Glendochart and eventually Loch Tay. Free communication along these routes was effectively stopped by the medieval Campbell castles at Kilchurn, Achallader, and at intervals along Glendochart and Loch Tay to Taymouth, and control of the local glens and the high grazing soon fell into Campbell hands, a fact that gave them considerable power. Wherever one looks, however, it would appear that they drove out, or adopted as tenants, an earlier, largely pastoral people.

There is a interesting and apparently unique association between the Glenstrae branch of Clan Gregor and the homesteads, in that their former seat at Castles Farm is named for one of these homesteads. A large number of these enclosures are in strategic positions and their area of distribution matches the lands traditionally held by the northern branches of Clan Gregor (see, for example, Taylor 1990, fig 9). This might of course be coincidental, but the specific link found at Castles Farm between the homestead there and a later high-status family points to continuity between the pastoral people of the Late Iron Age and later clans in the same area.

Despite their apparently defensive nature, defence against other humans does not appear to have been a consideration in the siting of crannogs, since anyone with a boat could gain access, and on a twenty-mile-long loch there must have been hundreds of boats. Nor were the cattle pens essentially defensive (Taylor 1990, 43), nor, for that matter, any of the prehistoric domestic sites of Perthshire, a point which is worthy of consideration. Professor Ritchie, in considering the siting of the Eadarloch crannog, considered that wolves were the obvious threat (Ritchie 1942, 19). The remote and central island on Loch Rannoch is the sole exception, and the defensive purpose in its building may well be a later introduction.

Historical Notes

As feudal superiors, the most long-lasting in Rannoch were the Robertsons of Strowan, an ancient native family, who were given part of the Lordship of Rannoch by a grateful Robert Bruce after 1314, only to lose it for supporting his descendant in 1745. Its subsequent history was described above. The rest of the old Lordship had a more stormy history. In 1473 the less than reputable John Stewart of Fortingall, and Neil Stewart, his son and heir, had from the King a nineteen years' lease of the lands and lordship of Apnadull, Glencoich, Glen Lyon, Strathbran and the rest of Rannoch, all former MacGregor lands, and probably Crown lands before 1473. The lease provided that they should have the lands of Rannoch free of all duties and services during the whole of this period, a plain proof that, so far as Rannoch was concerned, it was not expected to prove beneficial to the lessees. This lease does not seem to have been renewed, and after 1492 this part of Rannoch was disputed between the Campbell of Glenurchy and the Menzies of Weem until Robert Menzies got a Royal Charter of what was left in 1502 (Murray MacGregor 1898, 33).

However, Rannoch still proved unprofitable to manage. Clan Gregor seem to have resented being reduced without consultation to the status of tenants on land which they had occupied as freely as minor kings for centuries. One may well believe that their landlords were wearied and worried by them, since they were unruly and rebellious, and land-ownership implied responsibility under the Crown for law-enforcement as well as the right to collect rents. Thus we find, in 1559, that Mary of Guise, Queen Regent of Scotland, exempted Alexander Menzies of that Ilk for seven years from being legally liable for the MacGregors whom he had acquired (as he well knew at the time) with his estates in Rannoch - 'the auld tenentis and inhabitants thairof of the Clangregour' - since she agreed that it was not within his power to control them (Murray MacGregor 1898, 129).

The inability of Menzieses to control Rannoch gave an opening to Campbell of Glenurchy, who got a warrant to police Rannoch towards the middle of the 16thC, and immediately invited certain Macdonalds of Keppoch to move there. In 1558 or 1559, they began to rebuild the fort or castle of the Isle of Loch Rannoch, which had been dismantled by order of James V. By 1564, the refortification had been brought to the attention of Mary Queen of Scots, probably by the Duke of Atholl, to whom this new and unknown devil on the western horizon must have been even less desirable than the previous and more familiar one. In August 1564, the Queen wrote from Luncarty in Glentilt in Atholl to Colin Campbell to object to the MacDonald enterprise in crisp terms:

> "For to output the Clan Gregour and inpute vther brokun men of the like condition … we jugeit nocht mete nor expedient to be done. And thairefoir, our pledour is that ye causs the werk begun in the Ile within the said loch to ceiss; and not that onlie, bot all vther innouatioun quhairof your nychbouris may justelie complene, especiallie the inbringing of strangeris of vther clannis and cvuntres" (Murray MacGregor 1898, 139).

James Menzies of that Ilk, Laird of Weem, then recovered Rannoch and its island, but was prohibited from fortifying it, and Clan Gregor continued to occupy their lands there. Indeed, they had few options, since there was nowhere they could possibly move to. Pressed from all sides, the MacGregors continued to experience problems in Rannoch but somehow managed to present their case to Queen Mary, for, two years later, having been made familiar with the MacGregor point of view in the matter, the Queen wrote again to the Laird of Weem, again relieving him of responsibility for MacGregors on his lands but asking him, in turn, to allow the Clan to remain there, under favourable leases, since it was unreasonable to expect them to support themselves and be peaceful subjects without some land and possessions (Murray MacGregor 1898, 141).

Blood Rent[13]

The reasonable tone of this letter may be contrasted with the utter ferocity of arrangements for clearing MacGregors made under Campbell landlords only a few years later. One particularly infamous example was a lease given in Kenmore, on 18 May 1588, to Donald and Dougal McTarlich by Duncan Campbell of Glen Orchy, under which the tenants and their male offspring were to be allowed free use during their lives of the two-mark land of Glen Eurin, the one-mark land of Elir, and the half-mark land of Glen Katillie, in Lorne, on condition that they killed every MacGregor or MacGregor adherent they could lay hands on, both openly and privately, and continued to do so until the landlord was satisfied[13]. The term 'MacGregor adherent' probably meant families using other names but claiming allegiance on the ground of ancient common descent. There were many such.

The area where this legalised genocide took place is not possible to identify with total certainty, since these names have been adapted into modern Gaelic, but it is probably the hilly area in Lorne between the south end of Glen Etive and Rannoch Moor. At the south end of Glen Etive is a farm still known as Glenceitlein (NN 1447) and immediately to the south again is Glen Mheuran (NN 1444). On *Stob Coir an Albannaich* is *Coir' an Albannaich*, perhaps a corrie once used by MacGregors, or other fugitives from Breadlalbane, and in Glen Mheuran is *Eas nam Mèirleach*, 'the waterfall of the thieves, or rebels', perhaps a hiding place for refugees, or a place where several were caught. The one-mark land of Elir may be the open glen to the east, below *Sròn na h'Iolaire*, 'eagle mountain', (NN 1841), which might have been reduced to Elir in Campbell terms. If these locations are correct, even in part, the lease represents an attempt either to remove otherwise unrecorded MacGregors and adherent families from their old lands between Glenorchy and Loch Etive towards the end of the sixteenth century, or to prevent refugees from Rannoch from reaching and settling in Glen Etive and Loch Etive. Either way, the juxtaposition of landscape, placename, and intention produces a thoroughly sinister picture.

What is perhaps more deplorable than Duncan Campbell's campaign to clear his lands of native cattle herders is the method he chose - Gael was set against Gael, in a pattern that was to become only too familiar, and it may be postulated that already before 1600, the conflict between tribal law and the King's law had already begun to inflict irreversible damage on this, the last Celtic tribal society in Europe.

The infamous name of McTarlich does not seem to have thrived in this or any other area but, perhaps because their identity was so implacably reinforced by generations of persecution, the victimised Clan Gregor survived, as well as any Highland clan may be said to have survived. Nor did they survive in distant exile, but right there on their native heath. From various MS histories of the Rannoch family we learn that, notwithstanding the charter held by Menzies of Weem from 1502, the lands to the west of the river Ericht continued to be occupied by the family of Dunan until 1675 (Murray MacGregor 1901, 215). Meanwhile, Gregor of MacGregor of Ardlarich died on 31 July 1526 on the island of Loch Rannoch, which had been built by his ancestors perhaps two thousand years earlier, and the heir to the Clan chiefship, a young boy, was brought up on the island (Eilean nam Faoileas – island of the gulls) later in the century, a strange life, isolated amidst the wind and waters of the loch, on the edge of the underwater abyss, with seagulls for company. The last of the House of Ardlarich, in the direct line, is said to have been Captain Robert MacGregor who commanded the Rannoch MacGregors in 1745 for Prince Charles Edward Stuart, after which the improvers arrived and a steady stream of Gaelic natives began to move away from Rannoch and did not stop until they reached the most distant corners of the world. MacGregors continued to farm at Ardlarich until the death of Malcolm MacGregor there within the past ten years, but now the story is almost entirely in the past.

Bibliography and References and Notes

MacLeay (1818) MacLeay, Kenneth. *Historical Memoirs of Rob Roy and the Clan MacGregor.*

Gillies (1938) Gillies, William A. *In Famed Breadalbane.*

Murray MacGregor (1898 and 1901) Murray MacGregor, A G. *The History of the Clan Gregor*, vol I (1898), vol II (1901) Edinburgh.

Morrison (1985) Morrison, Ian. *Landscape with Lake Dwellings: The Crannogs of Scotland.*

Ritchie, J (1942), 'The lake-dwelling or crannog in Eaderloch, Loch Treig: its traditions and its construction.' *Proc Soc Antiq Scot 76*, 8-78

SHS (1909) *Scottish Forfeited Estate Papers.* Scottish History Society, Edinburgh.

Taylor (1990) Taylor, D B. *Circular Homesteads in North West Perthshire.* Abertay Historical Society.

[1] Gregorach, from Gaelic *greighear* 'herdsman,' with a collective suffix, was the original form of the name and is still found in the Dewar document of 1428, when fifteen local gentlemen gave evidence to a royal commission at Killin. The surnames McArthur, McAustillan, McCallum and McNab, all appear in their normal form but the three 'MacGregors' are listed as Duncan Gregorii, Dougal Gregorii, and Nicol Gregorii, ie, Gregorach. MacGregor appears to be a late change, based on a supposed person called Gregor, for whom there is no historical or traditional evidence.

[2] Ritchie says (1942, 25): 'No detailed description of the construction of such as the Loch

Treig artificial island has been published, and I have therefore given a reasonably full and illustrated account of a structure which may probably be taken as typical of the smaller lake-dwellings most common in Scottish fresh-water lochs.' This island was known in Gaelic as *Tigh nam Fleadh*, 'House of Feasts', and the Chiefs of Keppoch used the island for special meetings and feasts. Its original function, in such an isolated spot but beside the old track from Rannoch to Glen Spean, may well have been as a hostel or staging post. A summary of traditional evidence is given in Ritchie 1942, 15-18.

[3] The oldest date (uncalibrated) is 595 bc ± 55 (GU 1323) for Oakbank crannog (Morrison 1985, 24) which was confirmed, in a recent survey of crannog dates by B A Crone ('Crannogs and chronologies', *Proc Soc Antiq Scot* 1993, 245-254), to be the oldest date so far obtained for a crannog in Scotland or Ireland.

[3a] Clan Iain (I'n, Ian) Bhuide = children of yellow haired John.

[4] 'Streamlet of the feud, or bloodshed'.

[5] This reference comes from Jamieson's Scots Dictionary under **Cochachderatie**, an erroneous form of Tochachderach: "A MS in the Scotstarvet collection (Cal. Harl. 4609) records a charter to John Meyners [Menzies] of the office of Cochachderatie of Kyncollonie, and lands of Ferrochie and Coulentyne, lying in the abthanerie of Dull. It appears to be the same office as that of Tothia Daroche, as recorded in Niddisdale and both are corruptions of the Tocheoderache as given by Skene." Kyncollonie is probably Kingallin, behind Drummond Hill. Ferrochie is now Farrochil, near Aberfeldy.

[6] The only published study of Tossachdereth (Gaelic = Crowner) is by W Croft Dickinson, in *The Juridical Review*, 1941. He notes a charter of c1342 which grants the lands of "Ediramuky and Morinche in Desawer" (Edramucky and Morinish on the north side of Loch Tay) to the Tossach of Kyirctollony, which other charters make clear is Ardtalnaig, on the south side of Loch Tay. The existence of a Tossach at Ardtalnaig is not in doubt and there was still such an official in 1633. There is some other evidence from local history of a court site of some kind at Ardtalnaig.

[7] The existence of a Tossach (who may or may not have been a Tossachderach) in Glenlyon is more nebulous, depending on the name of a district there known as 'Toshich' which one would expect to mean land set aside for the support of a Tossachdereth.

[8] W Croft Dickinson refers to the existence of a Tossachdereth for the Earldom of Atholl at Tulliemet and Cuilt. An entry in the Dean of Lismore's *Chronicle* for 7 April 1516 records the beheading at Tulymat of William Strowan Robertson, and demonstrates the survival of judicial machinery for Atholl at Tulliemet then.

[9] According to Gillies (1938, 356), the Lochtayside Crerars or McIntoshes were "descended from a McIntosh of Monzievaird who came over the hills to escape justice." The crime from which he fled was the murder of a Murray at Monzievaird, who appears to have taken over the Tossachship there.

[10] Solinus, cAD200, describes the King of the Hebrides, who functioned under a matrilineal system.

[11] Other clans may well have settlement legends of apparently prehistoric date which associate them with crannogs, or with other sites, but they are not known to the writer. The focus here, on Clan Gregor, is not a matter of preference but a result of the lack of additional material.

[12] An account is given in MacLeay 1818, 345: 'The carving and stucco work which formerly had decorated the walls (of the main living-room) were still visible and shewed that it had once been occupied by persons of consequence and taste, whose manners, even amidst the desultory and rude customes of feudal ages, must have differed widely from its present possessors. The castle, for such was its style, built to

repress the attacks of maurading tribes, and secure a safe retreat in warlike times, anciently belonged to a chieftain of the Macgregors. It was not at this time of considerable extent, a great portion of it having become ruinous; but what remained preserved that massive and rude elegance displayed in the habitations of the ancient barons of the Highlands. It stood on a peninsulated rock washed by the waters of an extensive lake, which defended it on one side, while towards the land it was protected by an embrasured wall. For a century and a half it had been deserted by the owners and greatly fallen into decay; and for some time previous to our narrative, had become the occasional resort of banditti.'

[13] The Appendix (with acknowledgements to Mr Forbes Macgregor) below was published for Clan Gregor in 1981 and entitled "Donald and Dougall McTarlich's Band, a Document Unique in Scots Law. Rent for land held from Ducan Campbell of Glen Orchy is paid in MacGregor blood," and is followed by a condensed rendering of the Scots text.

[14] Editorial note – the Central Region Archivist in Stirling has in recent years acquired a large collection of MacGregor material – including personal letters of various Chiefs in 900 bundles = three bays of shelving – covering some 600 years – 1314-1921.

Appendix

McTarlich's Band

Be it kend till all men be thir pnt letteris We Donald
mctarlich and dougall mctarlich brodir TO BE BUNDIN and
oblist and be the tennor heirof bindis and oblisss us
faytfullie and treulie and aither of us induring oure
lyftimes and ane air male lawfullie to be gottin of
aither of oure bodeis To the richt holl duncane Campbell
of glenurquhay and his airis That forsamekill as the said
duncane is oblist to mak gif and deliver to me the said
dod ane lettir of tak during my lytfime and eftir my
deceis to ane air male lawfullie to be gottin of my body
during his lyftime all and haill his tua markland of
gleneurin and ane markland of elir wt ye pertinentis
liand in the lordship of Lorne within the sherifdome of
argyle and to me the said dougall during my lyftime and
eftir my deceis to ane air male lawfullie to be gottin
of my awin bodie during his lyftime all and haill his
half mk land of glenkatillie wt ye pertinentis liand in
the lordship and sherifdome foirsaids our intres to ye
lands rexve foirsaids to be and begin at our performance
and accomplishements of ye conditiouns following and na
utherwyis Thairfoir we being myndit heirunto and or evir
we sall craif possessioun of ye saids lands be virtew of
the conditioun and promes foirsaid maid to the said duncane
to us and understanding the clangregor to be manifest
malefactors and his Maties declair rebellis for sundrie
slauchters evill turnis and oppressions done by ya to
diveris personis his hienes liegis We bind and obleis us
and aither of us that we wt ye haill cumpanie and forces

we may or can mak sall incontinent eftir the dait heirof
enter in deidlie feid wt the clangregoure and sall
indure and continwe thair and in making of slauchter
upon thame and thair adherentis baith privilie and
oppenlie and sall be na manner of way or persuasion leif
the same or desist and ceiss thairfra unto the tyme the
said duncane campbell of glenurquhay find himself be
oure trauellis and diligence satisfiet and contentit wt
ye slauchter we sall do and comit upon thame and in
speciall abstract and wtdraw us thairfrae be him self as
alsua qll he find the way to mak ane aggreement and
pacificatioun betwix us and the clangregoure for ye
slauchter we sall comit upon thame sua that thairaftir
we may posses and bruik the saids lands to be disponit
to us in maner foirsaid according to ye tennor of ye said
assedatioun and heirunto we bind and obleis us and or
foirsaids faytfullie but fraud or gyle Subscrivit wt
oure hands as followis at balloch ye XVIII day of Maii
the zeir of god jai V^c foure scoir aucht zeris Befoir yir
witness colene campbell sone to campbell of
lawers gavine hamiltoun dold Mcangus and marreis
mcnaughtane.

Herewith an interpretation/condensed rendering of the above 1588 lease (band).

Donald and Dougal McTarlich, brothers, bind ourselves and our male heirs to Duncan Campbell of Glen Orchy and his heirs, Donald to have the two-makr land of Gleneurin and the one-mark land of Elir in the Lordship of Lorne in Argyllshire, and Dougall the half-mark land of Glen Katillie, on the following conditions: understanding the Clan Gregor to be evil-doers and declared rebels by his Majesty for various murders and other evil deeds, we and any others we can muster, shall immediately commit ourselves to killing MacGregors and their adherents, both secretly and openly, and shall continue with this slaughter until Duncan Campbell is satisfied with our diligence and content with the numbers killed and allows us to desist, and that he will also find a way to make peace between ourselves and Clan Gregor for having killed so many of them, so that, afterwards, we may possess our lands and enjoy the benefits of this agreement. Subscribed at Balloch (Kenmomre) the 18th of May 1588, before these witnesses, Colin Campbell, son to (Duncan?), Campbell of Lawers, Gavin Hamilton, Donald McAngus, Marcus McNaughton.

(S.McG.)

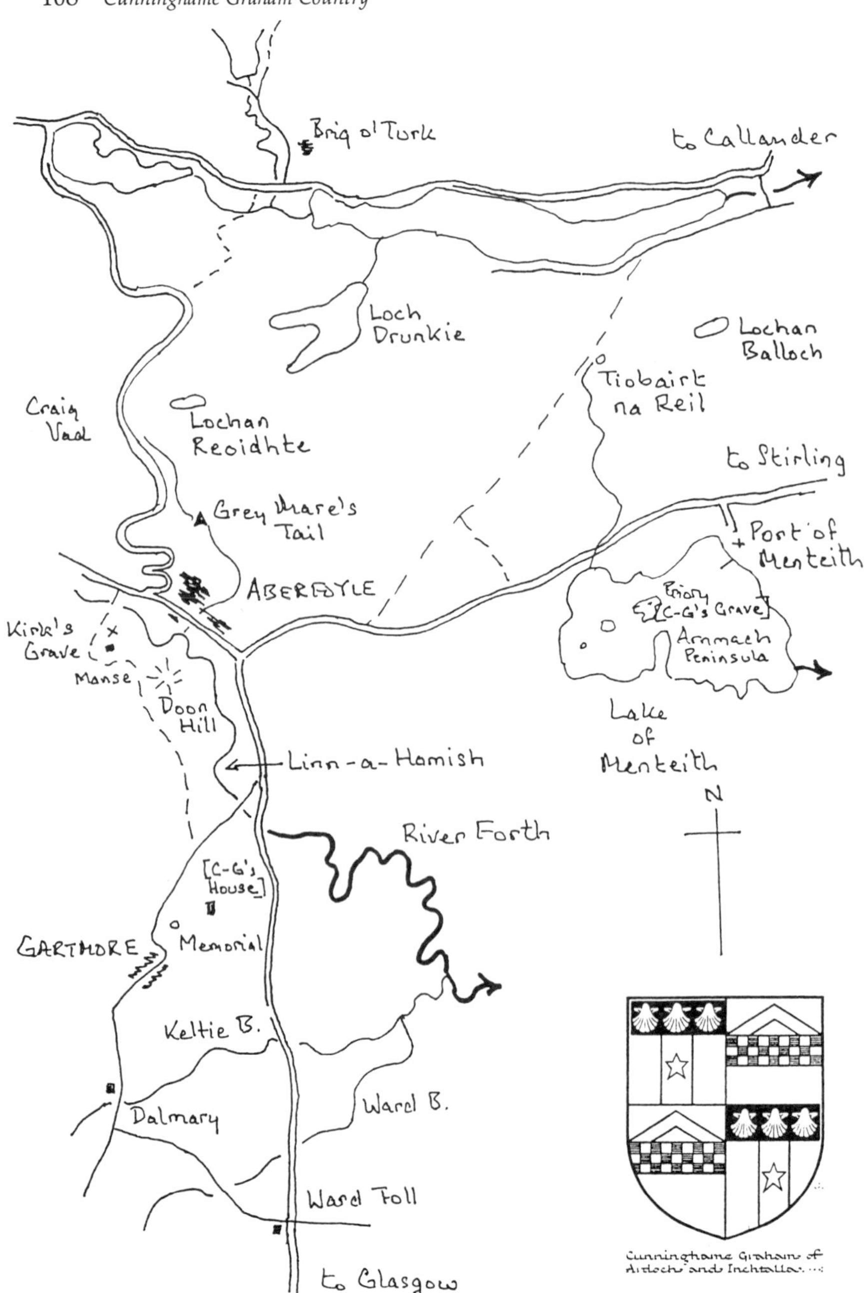

The Cunninghame Graham Country LS

Further Notes On The District Of Menteith

1. THE CUNNINGHAME GRAHAM COUNTRY
People of the Forth (9)

Louis Stott

1995 sees the centenary of the publication of Cunninghame Graham's first book *Notes on the District of Menteith,* a series of elegant, witty, and quite inimitable essays on the district he loved. This series of articles seeks to explore one or two further aspects of Menteith to celebrate the centenary.

"Does not legend have it that the very first barbarous and probably naked Scot who breached Antonine's Roman Wall was one called Graham and, thereafter, that rampart of the world's mightiest Empire was known contemptuously to our countrymen as Graham's Dyke."

Address on Founding of the Scottish National Party 1934

Menteith is a district with significant echoes of Cunninghame Graham, but they are rather neglected in comparison with those of, say, Scott's works about the Trossachs. They ought not to be; they are more genuine, and as evocative.

Andrew Lang considered the 'Gaucho Marxist' Robert Bontine Cunninghame Graham (1852-1936), descended from Robert the Bruce, as the rightful King of Scotland, and William Power characterised him as 'the noblest Scotsman of them all'. Both Joseph Conrad and George Bernard Shaw believed him to be one of the finest writers of English prose of his day – he was, as Trevor Royle puts it, 'a writer's writer'. He has left several short stories and sketches set in his calf country which are minor masterpieces, a distinguished writer describing a distinctive countryside in a memorable way (Walker 1982).

Cunninghame Graham spent much time in Argentina, helped to set up both the Labour Party and the SNP, and, with others, came close to bringing about a Revolution in Britain on 'Bloody Sunday' in 1887. Born in London, but bred on the southern banks of the Clyde, he lived at Gartmore from 1883-1901. He was a cosmopolitan figure and his work contains as many allusions to Spain, to North Africa and to North and South America as to Scotland. He was also, in some respects, an important Anglo-Scot. He lived at Ardoch, Dumbarton longer than he lived in Gartmore, but Menteith can be properly regarded as the Cunninghame Graham Country. There is a warmth, and pride in his heritage when he writes about Menteith.

Menteith is said by William Power to have a sort of 'crepuscular glamour', somewhat overshadowed by the neighbouring Trossachs, and frequently overlooked on that account. However, the Tourist Board now incorporates Menteith, bounded by the Highland Edge, within what is called the Trossachs, and Cunninghame Graham himself did not pay much attention to where the district began and ended.

His 'Notes ...' (1895) written "half in idleness and half out of that affection which is common to a man and trees for the soil in which they have been for ages rooted" is a highly unusual guide book which, because of its author's style is a delight to read. Graham's wit is illustrated by a notice on the first page: "All rights reserved except in the Republic of Paraguay". In this extract he describes some of the lochans of his calf-country:

> "Hard by Craig Vad is the desolate hill tarn known as Loch Reoichte. In the district there are many of these curious black hill-lochs, generally in peaty hollows, with the water black as jet, peopled with little muddy trout, and often overgrown with water-lilies. Each has its legend, as in duty bound. Loch McAn Righ, close to the Lake of Menteith, is sacred to the memory of a king's son, who, in the days when princes of the blood-royal perambulated the world at a loose end and unattended, almost lost his life whilst chasing wild deer, by his horse bogging down with him. Tradition hath it that one Betty or Betsy, for there is room for doubt on the forms of the name that the royal maiden bore, extracted him like a royal cork, from the mud and saved his life. The field is known as Achnaveity, said by Gaelic speaking men to mean the field of Betty. Tradition is in error in having woven no romance about the King of Scotland's son and Betty, but then how seldom tradition, on the whole, misses its opportunities in matters of the sort. Anyhow, nearby the field is the 'laroch' of the chapel of Arnchly, one of four chapels connected with the monastery of Inchmahome, so possibly the nearness of the sacred edifice prevented scandal making free with the Prince's or Betty's name."

Graham was inclined to be slapdash, and his hand notoriously difficult to read – for this reason some of his renderings of place names are highly doubtful, and a compositor working on the book in Glasgow became so dispirited that he packed his bags and went to London's *Saturday Review*. To his dismay, his first task was to set an article by Graham. However, a very similar story is told about Thomas Carlyle, so it may be a literary folk-tale!

One of his most interesting Scottish books, written after he had left Gartmore, is *Doughty Deeds* [1925], the biography of his ancestor Robert Graham, poet and politician, which begins with an evocative description of the country between Gartmore and Aberfoyle:

> "The old house of Gartmore, in the district of Menteith, was built, as tradition says, by the grandfather of the brothers Adam, somewhere about the year 1680. With low flanking wings, its perron and heavy mouldings over the windows and the doors, it was a perfect specimen of a Georgian mansion of the time. In the days of the poet's youth, before extensive planting was the fashion in the north, it must have looked a little bare, although the great beech avenue was possibly growing up. Rough woods of scrubby oak sheltered it from the north. The six great yews which I remember as a child were probably old trees when the poet was a boy. Great rushy parks led down to Flanders Moss, that had once been a shallow inland sea, as said tradition, and flowed up to the hill of Gartmore,

where a huge stone, known as Clach nan Lung (the stone of the waves) was there to testify."

Looking out of the windows of his home, to the left of the tall cedars, then perhaps just planted – they are shown as little trees in the drawings of the time – he could see the Grampians:

"The silvery waters of the Lake of Menteith, dotted with its two dark wooded islands, shrouding the Priory of Inchmaholme and the Castle of Inch Talla, the fortress of the Earls of Menteith, the poet's ancestors, and with the fir-clad promontory of Arnmauk cutting the lake almost in two halves, lay just below the hills. The moss that flowed right from the Hill of Gartmore through the Carse of Stirling to the sea bounded the lake upon one side.1 Upon the other rose Ben Dearg and Ben Dhu. Between them ran the Pass of Glennie, an old Fingalian track, whose stones, polished of yore by generations of feet shod in deerskin brogues, even today show white amongst the heather in places now disused, that once it traversed like a dull silver streak. Only two miles away to the north-west by the hill-road behind the Drum, crossing the burn where the stones form a rude bridge, lay Aberfoyle with the change-house immortalised by Walter Scott, and half a dozen black Highland cottages, all thatched with rushes or with ling. A rough hill-track skirting the waterfall, known as the Grey Mare's Tail, passing Craig Vadh and coming out upon the shore of Loch Achray, led to the Trossachs, in whose fastnesses lurked broken men from all the highland clans. Still farther westward rose Ben Lomond, looking exactly like Vesuvius, with its perfect cone and its top shaped crater-wise, when the white mists curled round its crest, steaming and billowing."

These two extracts from longer books are conventional essays, descriptive of scenery. His Sketches (Walker 1982) are more unusual and original, conscious efforts to achieve an effect. Most quoted is 'Mist in Menteith' , evoking the way in which the district can resemble the sea it once was, when the Firth of Forth extended to the fringes of Gartmore; similarly 'Snow in Menteith' and 'Pollybaglan'. Three short stories, 'Salvagia', 'At the Ward Toll' and 'At Dalmary', people the same landscape. The rather different feeling obtained on the moors above the Lake of Menteith is distinctively set down in 'Tobar na Reil' and 'Lochan Falloch'. 'A Traveller' is located to the south, about Balfron. 'A Braw Day' describes Gartmore House when Cunninghame-Graham was taking his leave of it. These stories and sketches – and others by him – ought to be recalled at the same time as the poetry of Wordsworth and the novels of Scott by visitors to the Trossachs, but they are missed, and remain relatively unknown. Two extracts, the first from 'Salvagia' [1899], which describes a bathing pool on the Forth, give the flavour of his 'sketches':

"A little river, in which, before the days of knowledge, kelpies were wont to live, flows past the town. Its glory is a pool (we call it linn) known as Linn-a-Hamish. Here the stream spreads out and babbling in its course wears the stones flat as proverbs in the current of men's speech get broadened out. The boys delight to throw these flat stones edgeways in the air, to hear the curious sound they make when falling in the water, which they call a 'dead man's bell'. Alders fringe the bank, and in the middle of the pool a little grassy promontory juts out, on which the cows stand, swinging their tails, and meditate, to at least as good a purpose as philosphers. The linn lies dark and sullen, and a line of bubbles rising to the top shows where the under-current runs below the stream. In a lagoon a pike has basked for the last thirty years. In our mythology, one Hamish met his death in the dark water, but why or wherefore no one seems to know. Tradition says the place is dangerous, and the country people count it a daring feat to swim across."

In the second from 'Lochan Falloch' [1909], describing Lochan Balloch, appropriately named, as it is in a pass or bealach in the Hills, however, he has changed the title because again 'falloch' means 'hidden':

"It is indeed a little hidden loch, lying so deep and unsuspected in its hollow between the hills that the first Celt or Pict who came upon it, ages ago, must straight have hit upon the name it bears. Nature seems, now and then, to have suspected that a time would come when all her secrets would lie bare and open to the prying eye of vulgar curiosity, and to have hid away some of her chiefest beauties in places where they are in sanctuary, hallowed from human gaze, which at the same time worships and violates them. So she set this little gem, remote, hiding it as a hind conceals her young, deep in the heather, underneath the tallest bracken and in a wilderness of hills. They tower on every side, bare bald and windswept, whilst in a corrie nestles the little lake, upon whose surface the wind scarcely or never preys, leaving it calm, mysterious, and unruffled, as if it held some secret, too natural for us to understand. If fairies still exist, they come, no doubt, from the Sith Bruach which guards the Avon Dhu at Aberfoyle, and sail their boats of acorn-cups and leaves on the black lakelet. Upon the little beach they run their craft ashore and dance on the broad ribbon of smooth sand which rings the leke, as a black mezzotint edged round with white. But if the fairies come, they come unseen, leaving no token of their passage but a few turned up leaves which they have used for boats, and the mysterious circlet of white foam in which float flies that have ventured further than their wings can bear them, and now wash up and down, as in some distant island of the South Seas drowned mariners may drift upon the beach."

There are numerous references in these pieces to Highland superstitions and it can be argued that Cunninghame-Graham's most significant local literary work was his introduction to a revised edition of *The Secret Commonwealth* (Kirk 1933), a shrewd analysis of Lang's edition and Kirk's influence. Kirk's work – subject of a further essay in this series – is a highly regarded, very detailed description of fairies in Scotland. RB typically, referred to Kirk as "the astral vicar of Aberfoyle".

Gartmore House (described above in *Doughty Deeds*), inherited when the estate was already in debt is just outside the village. It was greatly enlarged in 1780 by the noted classical architect John Baxter who was responsible for the beautiful bridge over the Tay at Kenmore, and, in the Trossachs, for Gartchonzie Bridge, near Callander. It is not surprising that RB found its upkeep beyond him; he sold it in 1901 to a shipping magnate, and went to live in the family's other house, finely situated beside the Clyde at Ardoch, near Dumbarton. Gartmore House became successively an Approved School, and the headquarters of a religious organisation. Access can generally be obtained to the policies by leave, freely given, of the owners.

A good account of Graham at Gartmore appears in Sir John Lavery's autobiography, *A Painter's Life* [1940]. Lavery was a leading figure among the 'Glasgow Boys' famous for portraits and landscapes, e.g. the picture of Loch Katrine in Edinburgh. Both he, and Joseph Crawhall, another of the 'Glasgow Boys' who shared a passion for horses with Graham, were particularly friendly. In 1895 Lavery came to paint portraits of RB and his wife. Lavery was a man of elegance and wit, who tells delightful tales:

> "John Burns had joined us on this occasion at Gartmore, for it was just at this time that they had both come out of Pentonville, where they had served six weeks' hard labour for their share in the Trafalgar Square riots over the queston of free speech – the two of them taking on, so they claimed, single-handed, the constabulary numbering five thousand. I asked them about their experiences in prison. Hard labour they considered less irksome than ordinary imprisonment, for with the former you were given plenty of coarse food, and time passed; while with they latter you were starved and left to pass the time in contemplation. There was a parson in the next cell to him, said Graham, who was in for "an old ecclesiastical failing". Burns was very proud of his biceps which he exposed, and Graham equally so of his agility with the foils, which he demonstrated from time to time with the aid of his walking-stick as we strolled in the cool of the evening.
>
> Graham purchased from the tramway company a wild Argentine pony that refused to go into harness. He named him Pampa, and insisted on my painting a picture of himself in complete cowboy outfit on the pacing steed. Then I painted him frankly in the manner, full-length and lifesize, a harmony in brown, which he christened "Don Roberto, Commander for the King of Aragon in the Two Sicilies" (The equestrian group he presented to Buenos Ayres, and the Commander was purchased by the Corporation of Glasgow). It was concerning the latter that Bernard Shaw said, 'He is, I understand, a Spanish hildago, hence the superbity of his portrait by Lavery (Velasquez being no longer available). He is, I know, a Scottish laird. How he continues to be authentically the two things at the same time is no more intelligible to me than the fact that everything that has ever happened to him seems to have happened in Paraguay or Texas instead of Spain or Scotland.' When I knew him at this time his finances were in a shocking state, and things were getting unbearable down at Gartmore. Suddenly he wrote to say that he could stand it no longer. Would I come down at once and see him end it all with Pampa, in a spot where I had painted a view of the Rob Roy Country that he loved? bI wired back, 'Ill in

bed, wait till next week.' Thus I postponed his death for forty years."

The portrait referred to by Shaw, who used Cunninghame Graham as a prototype both for Captain Brassbound and in *Arms and the Man*, is in the Kelvingrove Art Gallery, Glasgow. They also have a small bronze head by Jacob Epstein.

On the edge of the Policies at the Playing Field in the village is the Cunninghame Graham Memorial which was erected in 1937 at Castlehill, Dumbarton, later owned by the National Trust and removed to Gartmore in 1981. Stones marked 'Uruguay' and 'Argentina' are set into it, as is a memorial plaque, the inscription reads:

ROBERT BONTINE CUNNINGHAME GRAHAM
Famous author, traveller, horseman, patriotic Scot and;
citizen of the World as betokened by the stones above.
Died in Argentina   Interred in Inchmahome

There was a notable turn out for the burial in April 1936 which included many of his political and literary associates: James Bridie (O.H. Mavor), Wendy Wood, Compton MacKenzie, Alisdair Alpin MacGregor, and others. His funeral oration was delivered by the literary critic, William Power. The political activities Graham was involved in included, of course, the cause of Scottish Nationalism. The district came to prominence again in this respect after the second world war when the movement gathered strength in 1949, not for the first time, nor, one suspects, the last. The Scottish National Covenant, of which Graham would have heartily approved, was hatched by John MacCormick in Aberfoyle in April of that year. It would have delighted Graham that the first signatory was his distinguished relation, the Duke of Montrose.

Graham is buried beside his wife in the Priory of Inchmahome. This atmospheric spot has other literary associations, Alexander Scott (c1515-83), the poet, was the organist there in Mary Queen of Scots' time. Gabriella Cunninghame Graham (1861-1906) was a diligent religious historian and a poet whose poems impressed W.H.Hudson, one of Graham's many literary friends. There is a moving description of the way Graham dug her grave with his own hands in the biography by his friend Tschiffely. In addition to his contemporaries literary connections include a distinguished literary lineage. He was not the first Graham to bring distinction to Menteith with his pen.

Rob Roy MacGregor frequented the inn formerly situated at Chapelarroch, Gartmore which was the scene of one of his most famous escapades, his kidnap of Graham of Killearn. One of the best descriptions of this occurs in a celebrated account of the Highlands which RB avers was written by his first literary ancestor, Nichol Graham of Gartmore (1694-1775) in 1747. It is quoted by Robert Jamieson in his edition of Edward Burt's *Letters from a Gentleman in the North of Scotland*, also was used by Scott as a source for both *Waverley* and *Rob Roy*. Robert Graham (1735-1797) Nichol's son has one distinguished poem beginning:

If doughty deeds my lady please,
Right soon I'll mount my steed;
And strong his arm, and fast his seat
That bears frae me the meed.
I'll wear thy colours in my cap
Thy picture in my heart;
And he that bends not to thine eye
Shall rue it to his smart
Then tell me how to woo thee love;
O tell me how to woo thee!
For thy dear sake nae care I'll take
Though ne'er another trow me

This song was written down from a recitation by Sir Walter Scott who considered it to be a 17thC lyric, and included it in his *Minstrelsy of the Scottish Border.* Scott was later told that Michael Graham was the author and acknowledged the fact.

This 18thC Robert Graham had many significant literary friends. He knew both Smollett and Burns. His younger son, Nichol, married Sarah Blamire of Dalston in Cumberland. Her sister, Susannah Blamire (1747-94), visited her often. She was an important poet who wrote poems and songs in both Cumbrian and Scots. Hector MacNeil (1746-1818), the minor poet and novelist, may have met Graham, as Smollett did, in the West Indies. He was often at Gartmore 1786-90 when he lived near Stirling, and became engaged to one of Graham's close relations at that time, but the two poets quarelled and their friendship, and the engagement, was broken off. MacNeil dedicated some verses to Graham, but he later suppressed them.

"Hector McNeil was for a long time a close friend and intimate of Doughty Deeds. Many a long hour they must have sat together at Gartmore, where Hector was a constant visitor, over the bottle, alternately railing and praising that "poor slut" poetry, whom my ancestor, it would appear, had foresworn in such biblical terms. At least for a brief season, for to his dying day he never utterly forsook her charms.

How the friends fell out is quite unknown to me. It may have been that one of them had le vin aigre, and doubted of the inspiration of the other's muse, after a long "sederunt" at the festive board. However, neither seems to have held out a conciliatory snuff mull to the other, and the laudatory stanzas that McNeil had addressed to his friend and patron did not appear in the edition of his works of the year 1801."

A longer standing friendship of Robert Graham was with the Professor of Humanities from Glasgow, the poet William Richardson (1743-1814) who, in later life, lived close to Graham at Bridge End. John Leyden (1775-1811) dedicated a book of poems to a Miss Graham of Gartmore, but probably not the same one as McNeil was engaged to.

Menteith thus carries many echoes of its literary past. Cunninghame Graham describes its special qualities which will be the more readily appreciated by visitors with a knowledge of him:

"A dividing line, almost as abrupt as that between Portugal and Spain upon the Minho when Tuy and Valenca still glare at one another in mutual incomprehension, was drawn between the denizens of Gartmore House and the wild Highlanders, who lived only a mile or so away in the recesses of the hills."

There is no superior ancient monument in all Scotland to the Priory of Inchmahome, with its reminders of Mary Queen of Scots among the old stones. Delightful walks with stunning views link Cunninghame Graham's hill lochans and wells in the Menteith Hills, and, beside the infant Forth, the visitor walker can link half a dozen other sites connected with him and his literary ancestors.

References and Further Reading:

Graham, R.B. Cunninghame. *Notes on the District of Menteith, for Tourists and Others.* 1895.
Graham, R.B. Cunninghame. *Doughty Deeds: An Account of the Life of Robert Graham of Gartmore, Poet and Politician, 1735-1797, from his Letter-books & Correspondence.* 1925.
Kirk, Robert. *The Secret Commonwealth.* Eneas Mackay, Stirling, 1933.
Walker, John. *Cunninghame Graham and Scotland: An Annotated Bibliography.* 1980.
Walker, John. *The Scottish Sketches of R.B.Cunninghame Graham.* 1982.

EARLY TEXTILE INDUSTRY AND PLANNED VILLAGES IN THE ENDRICK VALLEY

J. Leiper (1)

The assumption that the Industrial Revolution in Scotland was urban based concentrates on the development of the steam engine and ignores the earlier use of waterpower in rural industry, particularly in textile manufacture. Starting with the rural corn and sawmills, the early "wauk" mills, and developing the technology of the transmission of power through gearing to such industries as brewing and distilling, coal-mining, the iron industry, paper and lint mills, and spinning mills for flax, wool and cotton – there was an explosion of inventiveness to harness the rotary power from waterwheels into mechanising what had been manual manipulation of some process of manufacture. So the early factories had to be sited where water was plentiful, near hills, and in valleys with good waterfalls like Endrick.

Fintry and Balfron, and Blanefield in the adjacent valley, were areas caught up in the early rural industrial development, prior to the urbanisation of industry 1550-1730, and then onwards 1730-1830, when the use of waterpower was at its height. In these districts the application of waterpower was adapted from the original corn mills, into the driving of lint, wauk and woollen mills, cotton mills and printworks, whisky distilling, agricultural drainage and, eventually, to the supply of electricity, from small-scale plants, using water turbines. All 25 mills (Figure 1), from Fintry down to Drymen and Croftamie, gave employment to over 2,000 people in the late 18th, to the early 19th centuries.

The early lint, wauk and woollen mills supplied mostly local domestic needs for cloth, and generally drew their labour from the local population – mainly those with a piece of ground who would be able to vary the amount of time spent between the mill and their own land cultivation. Handloom weaving was particularly suited to this division of labour – the weaver had the independence to organise his work from day to day, and was not tied to an employer. From the 1780s cotton textiles in the West of Scotland expanded rapidly. By 1812 the industry employed about 150,000 people in Scotland. By 1834, a factory inspector's returns for Lowland Scotland quoted 121 cotton mills. These were based on factory type production, far removed from the old style rural woollen mill. Factory employers, operating in a very competitive market, had to run the factories as continuously as possible, and the labour force had to respond to these requirements. Workers had to adapt to the monotonous regularity of the machine and the strict discipline of the factory clock. This did not fit the old style farming or craft practices, hence the men from these backgrounds resisted taking up employment in the new factories, and the records of employment show a majority of female and child labour.

There are two other factors to be taken into account to explain why things

ENDRICK VALLEY MILLS

Page Nos.	Map Key	Name	Parish	Grid Ref. N.S.	Remarks	Earliest date found
19	1	Gartcarron Mill	Fintry	66 85	Corn Mill	1452
20	2	Fintry Mill	Fintry	644858	Corn Mill	1585
44 54	3	Lowbridge Mill‡	Fintry	632863	Wauk/Lint/Woollen Mill	1585
83	4	Saw Mill (Fintry)†	Fintry	618870	Estate Sawmill	1837
22	5	Old Corn Mill on site of Cotton Mill	Fintry	616872	Corn Mill	1632
62	6	Culcreuch*	Fintry	615872	Cotton Mill	1792
23	7	Glenboig Mill	Killearn	602883	Corn Mill	1792
24	8	Balgair Mill	Killearn	Uncer-tain	Corn Mill	1741
26	9	Balglass Mill	Killearn	581884	Corn Mill	1607
27 55	10	Cowden Mill†	Killearn	567883	Corn/Lint Mill	1765
83	11	Cowden Mill*	Killearn	567883	Sawmill	1855
76	12	Gerchew Mill (Ballikinrain)‡	Killearn	573882	Woollen and Cotton Mill	1792
28	13	Kilfasset Mill	Balfron	555882	Corn Mill	1617
71	14	Ballindalloch Mill	Balfron	547883	Cotton Mill	1790
73	15	Endrick Printfield	Killearn	537880	Printworks	1792
29	16	Carbeth	Killearn	530878	Corn Mill	1750
30	16/1	Branshogle*	Killearn	547874	Corn/Saw Mill	1492
50	17	Gartnes Upper*	Drymen	501868	Woollen Mill	1799
46	18	Gartness Lower*	Killearn	502867	Wauk/Woollen Mill	1590s
31 56	19	Gartness Corn†/ Lint Mill*	Drymen	502866	Two buildings each with wheel gable	Corn 1494 Lint 1738
34 59	20	Blairfad Corn/ Lint Mill† (C) (L)	Drymen	496898	Also farm mill for threshing and grinding	(C) 1601 (L) 1772
35	21	Blarnarisk Mill (Drymen)	Drymen	472887	Corn Mill	1633
39	22	Buchanan Mill (Milton)*	Buchanan	445903	Corn/Saw Mill. The only mill with water-wheel intact	1590s -1662
41	23	Catter Mill (Corn)	Kilmaronock	477858	Corn/Saw Mill	1513
60	24	Catter Mill (Lint)	Kilmaronock	477858	Lint cultivated in Kilmaronock 1737 - church records	1737
83	25	Croftamie Mill	Kilmaronock	478862	Saw Mill	1819

* Building still exists † Ruin allows size to be taken ‡ Foundations of ruin only

happened as they did. When we look at the population records from about 1750 onwards, it can be seen how the numbers dropped dramatically in the agricultural districts, due to landowners' agricultural 'improvements' – combining small farms, enclosing land and improving the soil output and profitability at the expense of the smallholder who either accepted work as a hired farm hand or migrated to the developing industrial villages and towns, such as Balfron, Fintry, Strathblane, Vale of Leven and Lennoxtown. Fortunately, at roughly the same time big developments were moving immediately to the south in Glasgow and the Clyde Valley. The Glasgow merchants grown wealthy from successful Colonial trading, particularly in tobacco, were diversifying into acquiring land and becoming involved in industries producing consumer goods such as cotton wares, which could be traded for the primary cotton of the expanding American Colonies. These new 'merchant landowners' brought their business skills, energy and enthusiasm into this Endrick Valley to exploit the attractive water potential of particular sites – at a time when the textile industry in the West of Scotland was moving rapidly into mechanised cotton spinning, bleaching and printing. So that's the general picture.

FINTRY

Originally Fintry was based slightly east of the present village – where the parish church is – now called Clachan. The parish was totally agricultural but the village had a small woollen mill just downstream from Gonochan or Lowbridge (Figure 2). Lowbridge is an example of a simple wauk (or fulling) mill, with its earliest date around the 1580s, developing through a period as a lint mill (processing flax for linen), and then into an integrated woollen mill, with carding, spinning and weaving machines.

However, the big change in Fintry's story came in 1792, when the cotton

Figure 2 Lowbridge mill, Fintry.

mill was built. Culcreuch Estate had been held by the Napiers for five generations, but by 1778, they were in serious debt and sold Culcreuch Castle and its lands to the Speirs family for £15,000. Alexander Speirs was a wealthy Glasgow 'tobacco lord', a member of one of the leading merchant families who were ploughing their wealth into early manufacturing.

The second son of Alexander Speirs, Peter, established the Culcreuch Cotton Spinning Company, with various co-partners, including Cunnninghame Graham of Gartmore. The 1792 building of the mill coincided with the writing of the *Old Statistical Account* (OSA). Fintry's minister wrote:

> "This parish is on the eve of experiencing a great change, by the introduction of manufactures on a very large scale. A cotton mill is just erected on the estate of Culcreuch – 156' in length and 40' wide, which when finished will employ 1,000 hands."

But this was a very optimistic figure for employment and never reached. The mill built on the north side of the river (Figure 3), was linked by a new bridge to a specially built village called Newton on the south bank – now referred to as an industrial planned village.An essential part of the overall scheme required it to attract skilled workers to this 'green field site'. It is said that many of the key workers were brought from Dewsbury in Yorkshire. These mill workers houses, many still there today, were built in sets of four, upstairs and downstairs, were let out according to the size of the family – up to four children for the lower flats – and more than four to the top because the attics gave more sleeping space. The effect of this on the population was dramatic. The parish had 1,000 people in 1660 falling to 550 by 1780 and 348 in 1791 – all due to 'agricultural improvements' or 'clearances' as they are better known to some. With the building of the mill and the village, the population rose gain to about 1,000.

A self-contained rural industry, such as Culcreuch, in 1792, required three essential services – power, labour and communications. The power came from the Endrick River with a system of reservoirs giving enough water for a six weeks reserve in dry summers. The labour was attracted by the new village, and the mill employed about 400 people, just under half of that number being children aged 6 to 16 years. As for the third requirement, communications, in 1792 roads were dreadful – suited only to local horse traffic – not necessarily wheeled – most things being carried by pack horse. The OSA tells us that a combined effort by Speirs and Dunmore, who was developing his own industries in Balfron, obtained an Act of Parliament to build new roads in the district. These would be 'turnpike' roads, the most important one, as far as Culcreuch Cotton Mill was concerned, being the Crow Road from Lennoxtown to Fintry. Roads and Bridges to the west of Fintry and Balfron were also improved and the mill prospered in the early years – and it would have remained successful if the rest of the world had stood still, but it did not!

The steam engine was now perfected to rotary motion and the Glasgow industries could use this to advantage, with their easy access to coal supplies. Also there was a trade depression after the French wars affecting outlying

Figure 3 Culcreuch Cotton Mill, Fintry.

industry most severely. In 1837 the Culcreuch Company went into liquidation, then continued under new owners with a much reduced workforce until the 1860s. The *Stirling Observer* of 27th June 1867 says under the heading of "Fintry and Trade":

> "owing to the dullness in the cotton trade, the factory here has been stopped for a considerable time past, which gives to our otherwise animated village a very dull and dispiriting appearance. Many of the hands who were employed in the mill, have left the village to look after work elsewhere, whilst those who remain behind, are lounging about in a state of listless inactivity, hoping for better times coming soon."

By 1880 the mill was in ruins. However, the big waterwheel continued to be used for a sawmill, and from about 1900 to drive a water turbine for generating electricity led to the Castle for lighting, also the factor's house and some employees houses in the village. By that time Fintry parish population had dropped to 400 and the story had come round full circle.

BALFRON

The story of Balfron as an 'industrial planned village' starts with Robert Dunmore. Dunmore, like Speirs at Culcreuch, came from a wealthy Glasgow merchant family. His father, Thomas, originally owned all the land on which Glasgow University now stands, Gilmourhill Estate. Robert Dunmore was born in 1744 and died aged 55 in 1799. So he was one year old when Prince Charles Edward Stuart was worrying the Burgesses of Glasgow into supplying shoes and clothing for his Highland Army. He lived in what could only be described as a 'boom and bust' economy and did everything that a young upwardly mobile person could do. He matriculated at Glasgow University in 1773, was a member of the most influential set of merchants in Glasgow, a Burgess of the City, and a founder member of the famous Tontine Club in the fashionable Trongate. His partner in business in Glasgow was Napier of Ballikinrain and Robert made an astute move by marrying Janet Napier, the heiress to Ballikinrain in 1776 so acquiring the Estate covering Balfron and land to the east. He enlarged his landholding in 1786 purchasing Ballindalloch Estate to the north and west of Balfron. This gave him control of the river and all the surrounding land, essential for his plans to tap the waterpower.

He started by introducing a colony of weavers, building a few houses for them in the neighbourhood of the original village, now called Clachan. However, things really took off when Ballindalloch Cotton Mill (Figure 4) was built between 1789 and 1790 in partnership with James and Archibald Buchanan of Carston. Carston lies just west of Strathblane. The cotton mill was built on the banks of the Endrick, on the site of what is now Balfron sewage works, with its entrance gates beside the bowling green and the garage at the bottom of Buchanan Street. The building was much the same as Culcreuch, 150′ in length and 30′ wide with a waterwheel of 28′ diameter producing 35 hp – a standard design to fit the spinning machines being built at that time.

When the mill started in 1790 there were 390 people employed. Ballindalloch Mill had a total of some 10,000 spindles, with 100 spindles per

Figure 4 Ballindalloch Cotton Mill, Balfron (model).

machine, so there were a hundred spinning machines in the mill buildings. The main building had five storeys so there could be twenty machines per storey or flat. The early spinning machines of 1790 had one skilled spinner per machine, plus at least one child acting as a 'piecer', who attended constantly to any broken yarn under the machine, joining it up manually, to maintain the continuity of the thread. There were many other jobs in the mill dealing with the whole process from bulk cotton coming in in bales, to going out as a fine yarn to the weavers. Of the 390 people employed there were 120 men, 90 women and 180 children aged 6 to 16 years old.

This was the 'golden age' of prosperity for handloom weavers, and there were between 300 and 400 looms in Balfron. To house all these newcomers, Dunmore built the village, initially 150 houses with about a quarter of an acre of land each. The land was given on easy terms of feu duty to encourage settlement – the feu being raised later as the village prospered. The Parish Church minister, writing for the OSA in 1794, describes the houses as 'substantial', some three storeys high, slated and having upwards of 430 rooms with fireplaces. With 150 houses that means approximately three rooms to each house. His description continues:

> "The population of the parish has been in a fluctuating state in so far as regards the village, since the year 1790, seldom remaining stationary for a single week. In December 1792, there were in the parish 1,381 souls and of this number, the village contained 981, and of these 930 were new settlers" (i.e. only 51 native residents) and he goes on: – "There were besides about 200 people including all ages – imported into the village at Whitsun 1793, when the printing and bleaching commenced."

That refers to the calico printing works at Endrickfield, just down river from Balfron beyond what is now the Endrick Bridge.

These simple records of this development cannot hope to catch the 'boom town' atmosphere that must have existed while all this was going on, and everybody tried to settle down. This huge importation of people consisted of a completely different type of person – skilled artisans and mostly religious dissenters. Of course the dissenters' church had been based at Balfron since 1739, supported by dissenters from Kippen, Killearn, Kilmaronock, Drymen, Gartmore, Fintry and Strathblane, and was known as the Holm Kirk, originally at Edenbelly. But this new influx of people brought many different shades of belief; there were at one time five different church congregations in Balfron, and the parish minister considered there was a good deal of animosity between them. The farmers in the area were however cashing in on this population explosion, having now on their doorstep a profitable ready market for the increasing surplus produced by the improved type of agriculture. Balfron Spinning Mill and Printworks at the height of their prosperity had about 650 workers with another 400 handloom weavers as out workers in their own houses or small loom shops.

Dunmore's ownership of Ballindalloch ended in 1793/94 when his business affairs in Glasgow suffered from a commercial crisis and he went into liquidation. The mill industry at Balfron was continued by his partner Buchanan, linked to James Finlay and Company. It is not possible here to go into the Finlay period of the mill as that company was quite an empire, going much wider than Ballindalloch. There was a Government Inquiry in 1833 into working conditions and child employment in factories which resulted in restrictions, and by 1844 Finlay had decided to sell. The decision was based on viability reports which concluded that none of Finlay's rural mills came out superior to operating a mill in Glasgow. The mill continued under various owners with a much reduced workforce until 1893 when it was bought by Sir Archibald Orr-Ewing of Ballikinrain. In 1898 it was demolished.

STRATHBLANE

The main common factor that Strathblane had with Strathendrick was the possession of a good substantial river with beautifully soft clean water. This was essential for driving mill machinery before the days of steam engines, and for the various processes of cloth manufacture - bleaching, dyeing and printing – which all needed unlimited supplies of the purest water possible. But Strathblane's early industry was more associated with bleachfields. There were four in the 1790s but that did not bring in many people. The OSA says they increased the population by only 60 or 70. There was an inkle (or tape) factory built in 1793 which lasted until 1797. There were 22 weaving looms getting most of their work from Glasgow. But by comparison Balfron at the same time had 300-400 handloom weavers. So there was not the huge influx of workers experienced by Balfron and Fintry. The population rose later when the Blanefield Calico Printworks (Figure 5) really got going under Anthony Park Coubrough in 1841, increasing from a steady average 750 to about 1,400, and it stayed like that until the Printworks closed in 1898. There was also a Flockmill built in 1874, making material for filling mattresses.

There was an Inquiry in 1840 into the employment of children in Calico Printing in Scotland. It was estimated then that in the whole of the Scottish printfields there were about 5,000 children employed as 'teerers' which was the occupation of the youngest, a third of the total would be under thirteen. The definition of 'teerer' was the person who stirred the colours for the printing. The processes of bleaching, printing and dyeing and washing resulted in enormous pollution of the Blane and the Endrick, forcing Coubrough to instal an extensive system of filters downstream from the factory. Eventually Blanefield Printworks was absorbed into the Calico Printers' Association when Coubrough sold out in 1898. This Association was an amalgamation of 46 firms of printers, 32 in England and 14 in Scotland, which amounted to 85% of the British calico printing industry. It pursued a policy of closing what they considered to be outlying, uneconomical and old-fashioned printworks and Blanefield was one of them.

IN CONCLUSION

Balfron Spinning Mill and Printworks around 1800, at the height of their

Figure 5 Blanefield Calico Printworks.

prosperity, had about 650 people, with some 400 hand loom weavers as out workers in their own houses. Fintry had 400 in the mill and in Strathblane in 1841 a total of about 200 workers – 125 adults and 80 children – in the printworks and bleachfields, perhaps rising in busy times to 300. Like the mills at Fintry and Balfron, Blanefield suffered the competition from urban industries. The original reasons for siting industry in rural positions were being overtaken by new mechanical inventions, like the steam engine, the results of chemical research which avoided the long laborious processes of bleaching and dyeing with their associated need of copious supplies of water, and the mechanisation of spinning. So we see the end of the rural industries which had lasted for 100 years, roughly 1790-1890. A century is quite a good innings! It gave thousands of people employment in a reasonably healthy environment with good substantial houses considering the standards of that time. The success of Glasgow, on the other hand, was creating its own problems, with dreadful overcrowding and insanitary conditions, far removed from the 'planned village' concept.

Note 1 This paper is based on a 1988 thesis, a copy is in Stirling Central Library. Some illustrations of interest may be seen in *Balfron Heritage* by J. Thomson, 1991; also in *Strathendrick in Old Photographs* 1990, and *Fintry in Old Photographs* 1994, both by Stirling District Libraries.

Book Reviews and Notes (Historical)

The History of Dunblane. Alexander Barty, with additions by J.W. Barty and Elisabeth Okasha. Stirling District Libraries. 1994. ISBN 1-870542-29-0, 312pp. £15.

Originally published in 1944 by Eneas MacKay this book, out print for many years, is welcomely reprinted with an additional 15 page chapter briefly continuing the history 1900-1994. A victory in battle of Sir William Wallace at Sheriffmuir and an erect four sided stone called William Wallace whet the appetite at the start of the 43 original chapters highlighting events, people, places; religious and secular. Fifty pages take it up to the 16th century; onwards includes chapters on Argaty, Glassingall, Battle of Sheriffmuir, Kilbryde, old mills ..., Cathedral. This a well researched mine of varied information including references to sources, a dedicated life's work.

Polmaise 3 and 4 Mining Fatalities. Archie Bone. Privately printed. 1994. 103pp. Available at £4 from the author at 62 King Street, Fallin.

A memorial to miners who lost their lives from 1906 to 1965 reproducing *Stirling Obeserver* and *Journal* reportings.

William Wallace in Film and History

Wallace being much in the news with the Mel Gibson film, publisher John Donald has reprinted the outstanding 1986 biography by Andrew Fisher, 147pp, £8.95. Pressures on space have frustrated our intent to publish here a full updating of the three page review of Fisher by John Gilbert in our 1986 *FNH* 10 (copies available). Signet's book of the film is £4.95.

The unhealthy obsession of modern film-makers with the depiction of violence is fully exploited in Gibson's *Braveheart* vision of Wallace. There may be no bridge at Stirling and neither loch nor schiltrons at Falkirk, but images of violence, particularly of cavalry and infantry in battle, and the protracted torture scenes at the end, are indelibly imprinted on the mind of the viewer. While some aspects of the film, such as Wallace's ability to attract and motivate support and the duplicity or inconsistency of the Scots barons and of Bruce, would be supported in Fisher's biography, it is regrettable that the film-makers have not made fuller use of the book to get more than a vague air of historical authenticity. True history could be made just as dramatic as film 'glamour'.

In Fisher's biography what clearly emerges is the genuinely extraordinary nature of Wallace's achievement, a leadership of a whole wide varying community extended well beyond the purely aristocratic barons. Since Fisher, Professor Duncan has discussed how the Scots barons showed no real patriotism and were constantly divided and manipulated in his 'War of the Scots ...' *Transactions of the Royal Historical Society* ii. 1992, 125-137.

L.C./J.G.

THE FIRST SCHOOL BOARD OF TULLIALLAN, 1873-6: UNEASY TRANSITION FROM CHURCH TO STATE

Andrew Bain

Whatever local controversies may arise during the current changeover in educational administration from regions and districts to unitary authorities, it is unlikely that there will be any repetition of the outrageous scenes that took place in the parish of Tulliallan following the Education Act of 1872, which transferred responsibility for the supervision of education in Scotland from Church to State and required the establishment of locally elected school boards. Unfortunately, as events in Tulliallan between 1873 and 1876 illustrate, these boards were sometimes the scene for such conflict between the main religious denominations, and between the churches and more secular interests, that the transition from Church to State control was far from smooth. In the words of the *Alloa Advertiser*: "the School Board, the Parish School, and the Schoolmaster of Tulliallan have made no little noise, and attracted no little attention in the scholastic world".[1] The climax of that noise was reached in 1876 when the *Advertiser* described one meeting of the School Board as a scene which "far transcended in fierce strife, oppressive violence, and pugilistic demonstration any of the grand displays of the last three years".[2] Strongly condemning such behaviour, the newspaper considered sectarian dissension to be not at all "for the credit of our common Christianity".[3]

It might be thought that the writer was here making pointed reference to the standards by which contemporary local disagreements should have been settled. Unfortunately it was more than this: it was also a reminder of one of the major causes of such disputes. For almost 300 years in east-central Scotland, as elsewhere in the country, schools and teachers had been supervised by the Reformed Church.[4] By the mid-nineteenth century, however, some of the denominations into which that Church had recently divided were anxious to replace the educational control of the Established Church by a more representative structure. Strong criticisms of the educational situation were made in east-central Scotland as early as the 1850s by the Free Church[5] and the United Presbyterian Church[6], and similar views expressed nationwide were followed by the Acts of 1861 and 1872, which taken together removed and replaced most of the powers that had been enjoyed in education by the Established Church for three centuries. The second of these Acts saw the introduction of a national, increasingly secular, system which was to be administered centrally by a Board of Education in Edinburgh, and locally by nearly a thousand school boards of from five to fifteen members, depending upon population. Yet, as the example of Tulliallan shows, in practice the influence of the various Churches did not immediately disappear in what was intended to be an effective changeover to State control.

The strife that was characteristic of the whole three-year term of the first

School Board of Tulliallan, and which arose out of intense group and personal rivalry, is interesting now for three main reasons. First of all, it reminds us that although the changeover from Church to State may seem to us to have an element of inevitability about it, that is very much a later impression; to those living at the time the process appeared neither inevitable nor smooth. Secondly, the legal judgements that arose out of that strife were of some importance in defining the exact meaning of several aspects of the Act of 1872.[7] And thirdly, there is always human interest in a conflict that is sometimes saddening in its educational myopia, and sometimes hilarious in its acting out before the numerous and entertained public audience that was perfectly legally present at many of the Board's meetings.

The period from 1873 to 1876 began as it was to finish, with the disputed election of a School Board for the parish. It was clear from the start that there would be two distinct and opposing parties on the Board: one representing the Established Churches; the other representing the interests of the Free and United Presbyterian Churches, which had both resented nationally the traditional Established Church control of parish schools. Given this history of division,[8] the five members were unlikely to agree about very much of consequence in education. The situation was probably made worse by the absence in Tulliallan of a separate Free Church school, and certainly was by the presence of strong personalities on the Board.

At the very first meeting the sharp and deep division that was to bedevil the next three years was already evident. In a membership that comprised the parish minister, the Free Church minister, the United Presbyterian minister, a banker, and an estate factor, the chairman was appointed on a 3:2 vote, thus giving a narrow balance of power to the Established Church party.[9]

Shortly after the election, however, a petition was sent to the Sheriff of Perthshire alleging that the returning officer, the parish schoolmaster, had counted the votes erroneously, to the assumed detriment of non-Established Church interests.[10] Although no explicit accusation of vote-rigging was made, the returning officer was accused of three procedural errors. First, he had *rejected* voting papers on which the crosses had been entered in the space containing the candidate's name instead of in the space provided opposite the name. Second, he had *admitted* papers where the numbers of votes allowed (five) had been marked, not by crosses, but by perpendicular strokes (for example | | |). Third, in keeping with regulations governing all secret ballots, he had *rejected* certain papers that contained marks by which he considered a voter might be identified.[11]

According to national provision, accusations of this kind were to be settled on appeal to the sheriff. On the first charge, Sheriff Tait held that, although the crosses had been made outside the spaces provided, they had nevertheless been entered opposite the candidates' names, as was required, and that the voters' intentions were therefore perfectly clear. On the second charge, he ruled that, while required to mark their preferences in figures or crosses, voters were not bound by any reference in the regulations to the Arabic or Roman system of numbers. He therefore interpreted | to |||| as acceptable, but not ||||| since V was normally used as the Roman numeral for five. On the third charge, Tait considered that none of the marks objected to by the returning officer constituted a possible identification of the individuals who had made them.[12]

As a result of the Sheriff's redefinition of acceptable and unacceptable voting papers, there was a marked change in the results of the poll, and although the first three places were again taken by the clergy (in slightly different order) the banker was replaced by a general practitioner.[13] The consequence was that the Established Church party now found itself in a minority in the same ratio as it had previously enjoyed a majority. With the alignment again being 3:2, the stage was well and truly set for the three years of trouble that followed.

At the first meeting of the re-aligned Board there was no attempt at compromise or magnanimity. The Established Church chairman, who continued in office as a result of his unassailable first place in both countings of the votes, was immediately censured by those now in the majority party for refusing to accept the newly elected doctor's full participation in the meeting. A motion was also put, calling for the resignation of Thomas Buchanan, the Board's clerk-treasurer, who was both schoolmaster and an Established Church elder, and who had acted as returning officer at the election. Buchanan subsequently resigned, to be replaced by a clerk-treasurer more sympathetic to the non-Established Churches.[14] In forcing him out, the Board created one of its greatest future problems.

The remainder of 1873 and the early part of 1874 were characterised by repeated public displays of bad feeling between the two parties on the Board; and in the spring of 1874 matters came to a head when two issues arose which led to open conflict between the Board and its former clerk-treasurer. Both once again required appeals to outside authority.[15]

The first arose from the Board's earliest attempt to reorganise the schools that it had inherited as a result of the Act of 1872. In addition to the long-standing parochial school, Tulliallan had a second school, built at Kincardine in 1840/41, partly from parental subscription and partly from a parliamentary grant.[16] This won a high reputation locally, taking well over a hundred pupils, employing teachers recommended by the Inspectorate, and teaching geography, mathematics, French and Latin in addition to the usual subjects.[17] Free from partisan squabbles, its directors took decisions on grounds of merit, and in this context they appointed James Bryce as teacher on 28th August, 1868.[18] Bryce became much respected in the locality, and under him the school would have continued to flourish.[19]

Unfortunately for him it was a time of both national and local change. Under the Act of 1872, school boards could accept the supervision of schools that were offered to them by the managers or trustees, and in this way the Subscription School was offered to the Board. This led to a stormy difference of opinion in the parish, some arguing in favour of the transfer, and others protesting against it. Among those against transfer were the Established Church party, and several of them, including Mr Bryce, tried to buy their way into the Education Association, and so block the transfer. In spite of these tactics and the storm of opposition, the Subscription School was passed to the Board late in 1873.[20] With the school, of course, went the post of Mr Bryce, and very soon the Board made it clear to to him that they intended to dispense with the services of one not of their loyalties.[21] Since he was employed at the pleasure of the Board, he had little choice in the matter, but what choice he did have he exercised. By default, no agreement had ever been made with him about the length of notice required on either side, and he curtly informed the members that on his own authority had had closed the doors and sent the pupils home. When his letter was read out by the clerk, stating that Mr Bryce begged to intimate "that the successful applicant may have the school, as I am done with it", this part of the announcement was received with the public ribaldry and noisy merriment that so often accompanied or disrupted the business.[22]

Less than a month later, it was reported to the Board that Mr Bryce had been taken on as an assistant teacher by Mr Buchanan, master of Tulliallan Public School, partly perhaps out of friendship and partly perhaps as a solution to the Board's repeated refusals to grant him help in the school. The response was predictable. The clerk was instructed to inform both teachers:

> "that the Board refuse to recognise Mr Buchanan's right to appoint an assistant in the Tulliallan Public School without their sanction, and hereby give notice that unless Mr Buchanan dismiss Mr Bryce from the office which under his appointment he now holds, and unless Mr Bryce immediately cease to teach in Tulliallan Public School, the Board shall take steps to vindicate their authority as invested with the management of Tulliallan Public School".[23]

This threat was followed by an application through the School Managers for an interim interdict. The teachers did not oppose this, and Bryce withdrew from the Public School, yet the majority of the Board (and the Managers) decided nevertheless to proceed to perpetual interdict.[24] This was granted in the Court of Session by Lord Ormidale on the grounds that only the School Board could appoint an assistant; and Buchanan and Bryce were found liable for expenses.[25]

That Bryce's dismissal arose from his unacceptability, as an Established Church member and as a supporter of the group wishing to retain the former Subscription School, seems fairly clear. It certainly did not arise from any kind of reported inefficiency or lack of parental regard, for the presentation made to him upon his departure in August 1874 was attended by "a large number of the inhabitants of Kincardine, accompanied by a considerable number of children".[26] This acclaim and his subsequent success before returning to Kincardine in 1877[27] demonstrate the determination of the small majority of the Board to brook no kind of opposition and to be rid of him in spite of his wide acceptance among parishioners. It is not suggested that anything that they did was in any way illegal, and indeed in the longer term more radical reorganisation of schools did come about (in 1881), but the actions of the first School Board were lacking in the human qualities and skills that make for peaceful administration, especially in a period of transition.

The bad feeling that the Board's majority managed to build up with their widely respected and nationally well known master, Thomas Buchanan, led to yet another dispute that had eventually to be settled in the Court of Session. For a long time before 1872, parish schoolmasters in Scotland had been supported partly by a salary provided by the heritors, and partly by income from fees paid by the parents of their pupils. Traditionally, the master himself had collected both. Following the Act of 1872, schoolmasters received their salaries from the school boards, not the heritors. What was less clear from the Act was whether parish teachers in post before 1872 (the old parochials) should collect their own fees, or whether these were to be paid to the board treasurer before being passed to the master.[28] This ambiguity was the cause of another dispute between the School Board of Tulliallan and its old parochial, Thomas Buchanan.

Since the master refused to collect his own fees, the Board first of all endeavoured to have the treasurer collect them – in a very hostile classroom environment that produced booing and hissing – and then tried to force Buchanan to do so. He, however, continued to refuse, and took his case to the Court of Session, where, having had no fees during this period of conflicting views, he claimed for his loss with interest.[29] In due course the Lord Ordinary, Lord Curriehill, gave judgement in favour of the School Board, and Buchanan was found liable for costs.[30] In his Note, the judge deplored the lack of "a little mutual forbearance while the new system of National Education ... was being established in the parish", adding that since the parties "still kept each other at arm's length" the matter in dispute had to be judicially decided in a court. His judgement found that Buchanan's claim was based upon an erroneous and untenable construction of Section 53 of the 1872 Act, which specified that "fees shall be paid to the treasurer". In his view, Buchanan had wrongly taken this to mean the actual physical collection from pupils and parents, whereas the Act's intention was that, although fees would be a part of the school fund and so pass through the treasurer's accounts, they were not necessarily to be collected by the treasurer himself.[31]

Despite finding in its favour, Lord Curriehill could not resist making adverse comment upon the management style of the Board, maintaining that:

> "It might have been more courteous of the Board to have explained their views to the pursuer before returning to the old system of collecting the fees, and the resolutions might have been expressed in less imperative terms".

He also made the point that if something like his own careful and courteous rewording of the Board's letter to Buchanan had been followed, no ill feeling need have arisen. He suggested that the Board really intended to say:

> "We wish you, the teacher, to continue to have the fees as part of your emoluments as heretofore. We have not the facilities for collecting them which you have; but you will collect them and appropriate them in the same way as you used to do before 1872, and we will assist you in case of difficulty with our statutory powers of prosecution; and all that you have to

> do is to inform our treasurer how much you collect in name of fees, and how much remains in arrear."

Reworded in this way, Lord Curriehill considered that the proposal that Buchanan should collect his own fees was not unreasonable, and even had certain advantages for him; it was assuredly not contrary to the Act's intentions.[32]

Lord Curriehill was quite right to draw attention to the ideal way of resolving the situation, but what he could not give weight to – and was perhaps not even aware of – was the long and emotional history of disputed control, and of personal grievance arising out of the Board's refusals to grant Buchanan proper assistance in the school. It must seem to us now that some of the difficulties experienced by the Tulliallan School Board need not have arisen had Buchanan been retained as clerk-treasurer instead of being dismissed for obvious sectarian reasons. Had he continued in post, discussion at an informal level might have replaced dependence upon what Lord Curriehill had called "imperative terms". As it was, there was little room in the proceedings of the School Board for the quiet reasonableness advocated by the judge.

In January 1875 Buchanan's appeal against the judgement was put on the Roll, and was heard in June by seven judges, who upheld the previous decision against him, with his added liability for further expenses.[33] For Buchanan the case was a costly and frustrating experience. Yet, in the wider context of Scottish education at a critical time of transition, it at least settled authoritatively a point of interpretation in the Act of 1872 which required clarification, and which had previously given rise to varied judgements in the county courts.[34]

One battle may have been over, but the war continued. In May 1875, when Buchanan requested a share of the government grant that his school had earned for that year, his request was passed by the School Board majority to the equally unsympathetic Managers, who under the Act of 1872 had been appointed by the Board to be responsible for routine administration. Predictably the Managers, chaired by the Free Church minister, refused Buchanan's request on the grounds that they were responsible for keeping cost to the ratepayers as low as possible.[35]

Yet that was not to be the end of the Board's lack of consideration. In August 1875 the majority decided to suppress Buchanan's school, and also one maintained by Lord and Lady Osborne, in favour of Kincardine Public School. When word of this resolve became public, a meeting of indignation and protest was called, and its noisy deliberations eventually produced a strong petition that was sent off to the Board of Education in Edinburgh with 800 signatures attached, representing a considerable proportion of the adult population.[36] Thus, when the Board applied formally for permission to concentrate the education of all pupils in Kincardine Public School, the Board of Education, taking account of the petition and after investigation of the local situation, turned down the application on the grounds that:

> "it may ultimately be expedient to concentrate the Public School teaching in one building, but that they were not satisfied that it would be advisable to do so at the present time and under present circumstances."[37]

By this time it was clear to most observers that the Board, with its 3:2 majority in favour of non-Established Church views, did not adequately represent a significant number of the inhabitants of the parish. It was a situation that could be resolved only by the election of a new School Board, but even this brought no immediate end to the conflict, and there was one more appeal to external legal intervention.

The first meeting of the new Board on 24th April 1876 saw continuation of the wrangling that had characterised the first three years. Only three members of the previous Board had been re-elected, and representatives of the Established Church were now in a majority. The first dispute arose over a Free Church motion to continue the traditional practice of beginning meetings with prayers, which was defeated.[38] Further disputes reflecting sectarian differences on the Board followed,[39] but fortunately for the long-term good of the parish this abrasive composition of the Board was not to enjoy a long life.

Mr Duncan Wright, a Free Church sympathiser and one of the now discontinued Managers, petitioned the Sheriff of Perthshire, claiming that the recent election had been invalid as a result of the idiosyncratic behaviour of the returning officer, the Rev. Mr Smeaton, who was the parish minister and had been chairman of the previous Board. The Rev. Smeaton was criticised on several counts. First of all, he had apparently kept no proper records during the election process. Secondly, against regulations, he had recorded his own vote. Thirdly, he had offered the use of his carriage to certain electors (presumably those of like mind). But what had seemingly caused most offence was his exuberant delight when the votes had been counted. "We've won! We've won!" he was heard to chant.[40]

Although Sheriff Graham judged that the last two factors were not of themselves sufficient to disqualify Smeaton, when these were taken in conjunction with the recording of his own vote and his failure to ensure proper records that could be later scrutinised for alleged errors, there was no doubt that the election was invalid. He therefore passed his judgement to the Board of Education in Edinburgh, whose province it was in his view to produce a remedy.[41]

That remedy was a long time coming, and in the meantime the original School Board continued to meet in acrimonious division over every piece of business that could not be delayed until the Board of Education pronounced. One such occasion is not without its humorous side. When there was a clash between the non-Established Church majority of the Board, who wished to discuss the Sheriff's judgement, and the Established Church chairman, who wished first to read a prepared protest, the chairman appealed direct to the attendant audience. Considerable disturbance immediately arose, whereupon the Board decided to retreat for the sake of peace to the Free Church hall and there met in private. On their way, the members were followed by a raving, hooting crowd, and when the gates were locked, several of the crowd leaped the wall and attempted to force admission. Only the timely arrival of the police officer compelled them to retire, thus allowing the meeting to continue – although still in a disputatious frame of mind.[42]

Resolution of the problem set by the Sheriff's declaring the election invalid came at last when the Scotch Education Department in London ordered a new one. Even then, however, the process was not straightforward. The new Board first met with only three members because five of the eight nominees withdrew, and although these were all from the Free and United Presbyterian Churches, their reasons for withdrawing are far from clear, and there was much contradictory public comment upon their doing so.[43] Subsequently, two more members were coopted from those who had obtained most votes in the earlier proceedings.[44]

Thus for the first time since 1872, although there was still a connection between individual members of the Board and the local church congregations to which they belonged, no clergyman was directly involved. The new chairman, an estate factor who had served on the previous Board, undertook from the start to "do all in his power to discharge the business of the Board satisfactorily".It was a promise that, on the whole, he was able to keep, and his less intensely sectarian, more pragmatic, approach soon produced results: the word 'unanimously' began to appear much more frequently in the minutes.[45]

Over the course of the next three years, though not everyone was entirely satisfied with its decisions, at least the Board itself ceased to display in public that notorious and divided behaviour which had previously been almost habitual. Proceedings did not have to be abandoned; fighting no longer broke out among the audience; the local policeman was no longer needed to restore order; and appeals, either to the Sheriff or to the Court of Session, for the resolution of clergy-led disputes were no longer required.[46] As Lord Curriehill had wished, the new system of national education introduced by the Act of 1872 was at last given a chance in Tulliallan without being impaired by sectarian strife in the very organisation intended to foster the transfer.

Contemporary assessment of the work of Tulliallan Parish's first School Board depended very much upon where one's sympathies lay, and ranged from the belief of the majority on the Board that "we have justified the confidence placed in us in 1873" to the belief of others in the parish that the interests of education had been sacrificed to sectarian bigotry.[47] From today's perspective we should probably incline to Lord Curriehill's detached and balanced view that "a little mutual forbearance" would have assisted the early establishment in Tulliallan Parish of the benefits of national education. To the historian it seems a pity that the attitudes of forgiveness and cooperation that were expressed so clearly in this part of Scotland at the time of the Disruption of 1843 were not continued into the practice of the Tulliallan church parties thirty years later.[48] Such cooperation and understanding would have made the transition in 1873 much easier and have led much sooner to a search for pragmatic and agreed solutions to local problems of educational reorganisation. As it was, the possible benefits of pragmatic response to change were resisted for sectarian reasons, decisions were confused by personal animosity, able teachers were undervalued, their work was disrupted, and beneficial, long-term amalgamation of school buildings was delayed.

On the whole, one might conclude that the results of those disputes highlighted here which went to legal settlement contributed less to the educational good of

Tulliallan than they did to the gradual accumulation of national legal clarification that follows major legislation. There is little doubt that the judgements given by the Sheriff of Perthshire and by the Court of Session were helpful in coming to a national understanding of the full meaning of the Act of 1872.[49] In Tulliallan itself, however, the first School Board's preference for confrontation and litigation led to a public weariness with strife that showed itself in the composition and policy of the second Board from 1876 until 1879. For a local historian, significant legal decisions do not entirely compensate for the bad feeling, the lost ideals, the maladministration, and the lost opportunities. From a later, more ecumenical and more secular, standpoint the prevailing feeling is one of regret that such backward-looking attitudes and such personal bitterness among the later nineteenth century Tulliallan churches should have marred the initial effectiveness of an Act of Parliament that was, ironically, intended to settle so many of the inherited sectarian difficulties and conflicts in Scottish education.

ACKNOWLEDGEMENT

I am most grateful to Mr James Sharp for lending me photocopies of the minutes of the School Board, of the Managers, and of the Education Association responsible for the Subscription School.

NOTES AND REFERENCES

1. *The Alloa Advertiser*, 7 November, 1874.
   James Sharp has called these *The Troubled Years* in his collection of the reported proceedings of the School Board of Tulliallan (1994). See his work for numerous instances of dispute in this long conflict. [(51)]
2. *Advertiser*, 29 July, 1876.
3. ibid, 17 June, 1876.
4. For a fuller discussion of the ways in which the Church supervised schools in east-central Scotland, see Bain, A.: *Patterns of Error* (1989) and *From Church to State* (1993).[(51)]
5. Free Church Presbytery of Stirling, 24 January, 1854.
6. U.P. Presbytery of Cupar, 20 March, 1855.
7. Tod J.: *Handbook of the Education (Scotland) Act, 1872* (Edinburgh, 1873); Graham, J. E.: *A Manual of the Acts relating to Education in Scotland* (Edinburgh and London, 1902).
8. For a common national overview of the situation post 1843 see, for example, Drummond, A. L. and Bulloch, J.: *The Church in Victorian Scotland, 1843-1874* (Edinburgh, 1975), particularly pp. 90-102 in Section 4.
9. Minutes of the School Board of Tulliallan, 21 April, 1873.
10. *The Alloa Advertiser*, 12 April and 3 May, 1873.
11. A useful summary of the issues is contained in Tod, pp. 257-8.
    See also Scottish Record Office, SC 49/7/975 and SC 44/22/5829.
12. Tod, pp. 257-8; S.R.O. SC 49/7/975 and SC 44/22/5829.
13. *Advertiser*, 10 May, 1873 gives the first and second counts. Both parties had increased totals, but the Free Churches gained nearly three-quarters of the extra votes, and led by 488 to 376 votes.

14. School Board, 8 and 19 and 20 May, 1873.
15. School Board and *Advertiser* for July, 1873 until the end of the year.
    How all this was assessed by the *Advertiser* is reported particularly on 19 July, 2 and 16 August, and 29 October, 1873.
16. Minutes of the Kincardine and Tulliallan Education Association, 20 May, 1840; 23 January, 1841.
17. The Association's Rules and Regulations of 15 May, 1846 give in No. 4 the subjects to be taught.
18. Minutes of the Association, 26 August, 1868.
19. *Advertiser*, 8 August, 1874.
20. ibid, 22 and 29 October, 1873. See also *The Alloa Journal*, 16 August, 1873.
21. Minutes of the Association, 8 April and 25 July, 1873.
22. *Advertiser*, 25 April, 1874; School Board, 11 May, 1874.
23. School Board, 11 May and 1 June, 1874; Managers, 5 June and 31 August, 1874.
24. School Board, 19 May and 15 June, 1874; Managers, 19 June, 1874.
25. SC 49/1/108; SC 49/8/9; Graham, p. 279; *Advertiser*, 5 September, 1874. It is interesting that the Education Department in London had refused to express an opinion. (Managers, 6 July, 1874).
26. *Advertiser*, 8 August, 1874.
27. School Board, 24 January, 1877.
28. Education (Scotland) Act, 1872, Sections 43, 48, 53 and 55.
29. School Board, 8 January, 20 February, 20 and 31 March, 11 and 19 May, 1874. CS 246/161/1.
30, CS 246/161/1.
31. See the discussion of the case brought by Thomas Robert Buchanan against Tulliallan School Board in November, 1874 regarding arrangements for the collection of the schoolmaster' fees (CS 246/161/1, Note by Court).
    The Board of Education, possibly recognising the source of conflict, refused on policy grounds to send an Inspector on a surprise visit to test the organisation and discipline in the school (Managers, 30 October, 1874; 6 March and 8 April, 1875.
32. CS 246/161/1, Note.
33. CS 246/161. In his comments the Lord President said he thought it desirable that the parties, now that the Court had given an opinion, "should endeavour to make affairs work a little more smoothly than they had done upon both sides".
34. Discussion in *Advertiser*, 19 June, 1875. The Managers refused to collect the fees owed (Managers, 10 January, 1876).
35. School Board, 6 May, 1875; Managers, 14 December, 1874, 11 May, 1875.
36. A full report of the public indignation meeting appears in *Advertiser*, 7 August, 1875. The steps taken by the Managers are detailed in their Minutes for 28 July, 7 October and 8 November, 1875.
37. *Advertiser*, 13 November, 1875. The *Advertiser* fills a gap in the Board's records between 28 July, 1875 and 21 February, 1876.
    For a full account of the Board of Education's decision see Managers, 8 November, 1875; Board, 21 February, 1876.
38. School Board, 24 April, 1876.
39. ibid, 6 and 11 May, 3 June, 1876.
40. Very full accounts of the petition and proceedings are given in the *Advertiser* of 3 and 10 June, 1876; and in the *Journal* of 3 June, 1876.
41. Full reports of the Interlocutor and Note are in the *Advertiser* of 17 June, 1876. See also SC 44/22/5939. School Board, 12 June, 1876 includes a detailed report of the judgement and the School Board's response.

42. *Advertiser*, 17 June, 1876.
    Journal, 29 July, 1876; School Board, 21 July, 1876.
43. School Board, 25 August, 1876.
    Advertiser, 26 August, 1876.
44. School Board, 25 August, 1876; *Advertiser*, 26 August, 1876.
    Questions about the procedure inevitably arose (*Advertiser*, 2 September).
45. School Board, 25 August, and 2 December, 1876. For example, Buchanan's long-standing request for a share of the Government grant was agreed unanimously (Board, 13 September and 13 December, 1877).
46. Letters expressing various opinions continued to be received by the local papers: for example, *Advertiser*, 26 August, 2 September, 2, 9 and 23 December, 1876. *Journal*, 9 September, 1876.
    Clergymen did not disappear for ever from the School Boards: there was one on the Board of 1879-82; three were on the Board of 1882-85.
47. See a number of letters to the *Advertiser* of 1 and 8 April, 1876.
48. *Stirling Journal and Advertiser*, 29 May, 1843; Free Church Presbytery of Dunfermline, 3 March, 1846.
49. Additional shortcomings of regulation experienced locally were: the difficulties generated by having only five members; allowing a retiring chairman to become returning officer; allowing public participation at Board meetings; and the slowness of response of a new centralised authority.

Further reading for interest and reference

50. *From Church to State – the significance of the Education Act of 1861 in east-central Scotland*, by Andrew Bain. 150pp. 1993. A. Bain, 22 Clarendon Road, Linlithgow. £6.50.
51. *Tulliallan School Board – the troubled years 1872-6*. James Sharp. c130pp. priv. print. (available in libraries – Alloa, Dunfermline, Kincardine and Central Region Archives, Stirling).

Book Reviews and Notes (Historical)

Seeking Mr Hyde: Studies in Robert Louis Stevenson. Tom Hubbard. Scottish Studies Centre. Gutenberg University, Mainz. 1995. 115pp. ISBN 3-361 49107 7. DM45.

Explores cultural cross currents in late 19C and beyond, suggesting relationships with such European figures as Dostoevsky, Rilke, Jung and Marcel Schwob. Concentrating first on *Jekyll and Hyde,* and on puritan repression versus unbridled energy, the book points to deeper universal significances of the Hyde figure and its related archetypes in other works by RLS and other literatures and cultures. Chapters are entitled – Hellish Energy, Masks and Mirrors, Damnation of Faust, and Underground and Labyrinths.

T.H.

Ring of Words. Scotland literary topography series by Louis Stott. 1995. Creag Darach Publications. *Argyll.* 40pp. ISBN 1 874585 04 0 £3.95 and *Literary Loch Lomond.* 40pp. ISBN 1 874585 05 9. £3.95.

Valuable well presented guides alphabetically by places, with key list of selected sites, and indexes of authors – occasional illustrations and frequent quotations.

The Life and Times of Falkirk. Ian Scott. 1994 and 1995. 192pp. John Donald. ISBN 0 85976 386 2. £9.95.

A well presented survey by a leading member of the Falkirk History Society with emphasis on researches of the last 20 years since Lewis Lawson's *History of Falkirk.* It highlights particularly – the Legions of Rome, Christians and Barons, the Livingstones of Callendar, Kirk and Courts, Cattle Trysts and Highland Armies, Iron and Canals, Church and School in Victorian Times, Falkirk Today and Tomorrow. This is readable, well illustrated, fine value to cater for the awakening interest in fascinating people and events spanning the changing times from the oyster eaters, through the Romans on to the Industrial Revolution and into recent times for this Forth area, central to Scotland's history. The author is now Director of the Saltire Society.

The Ochils – place names, history, tradition. Angus Watson. Nov. 1995. 160pp. Perth and Kinross Libraries. £10.95.

A nicely produced gazetteer style source, a wealth of information much of it little known.

AUTHORS' ADDRESSES FOR FORTH NATURALIST AND HISTORIAN, VOLUME 18

Bain, Andrew, 22 Clarendon Road, Linlithgow.

Devaney, Maria, Smith Art Gallery and Museum, Stirling, FK8 2RQ.

Dixon, George A., Regional Archive, Burghmuir Estate, Stirling, FK7 7PY.

Harrison, S. J., Environment Science, University of Stirling, FK9 4LA.

Henty, C. J., c/o Psychology, University of Stirling, FK9 4LA.

House, Syd, Conservator, Forestry Authority, York Place, Perth, PH2 8EP.

Leiper, J., 13 Muirpark Way, Drymen, G63 0DX.

McGregor, Sheila, 8 Greenhill Place, Edinburgh, EH10 4BR.

Stott, Louis, Browser Bookshop, 25 High Street, Dunblane, FK15 0EE.

Wewetzer, Silke F. K., Geography, Purdie Building, University of St Andrews, KY16 9ST.

THE FORTH NATURALIST AND HISTORIAN

A charitable body to promote Central Scotland heritage/environment (SCO 13270). Member of the Scottish Publishers Association.

Set up in 1975 to provide a focus for interests and publications of naturalist and historical studies for the central Scotland area. The annual volumes act as an authoritative successor to the *Transactions of the Stirling Field and Archaeological Society* 1878-1939.

Orders/enquiries to Hon. Editor L. Corbett, University of Stirling FK9 4LA, tel: (01259) 215091; fax (01786) 464994, telex 777557 Suniv.G, email dsm2@stirling.ac.uk. Titles here are FN&H in print, some are shared, associated or commissioned. Many are available at good bookshops. P marked items are pamphlet versions of papers in the annual volumes.

1 AIRTHREY AND BRIDGE OF ALLAN. Rev. 1995 40pp, FN&H. (0-9506962-6-9). £1.85.

2P ALLAN MAIR – last person executed in Stirling, by C. Mair. pph 80p (p&p 50).

3P ALLOA AND HILLFOOTS TEXTILE INDUSTRY. G. Scobie. pph 60p (p&p 50).

4P ALLOA PORT, SHIPS AND SHIPBUILDING. pph. by J. Archibald. 50p (p&p 40).

5 ALLOA TOWER – 1987, 40pp. CFSS. £1 (p&p 60).

6P BRIDGE OF ALLAN – HERITAGE OF MUSIC and MUSEUM HALL. pph. £1 (p&p 50).

7P BRIDGE OF ALLAN – QUEEN OF SCOTTISH SPAS. pph. 80p (p&p 50).

8 CENTRAL SCOTLAND – Land, Wildlife, People by L. Corbett et al. 230pp. 1994. Bargain price £5 (p&p £2). (SBN 1-898008.00.0).

9P DICKENS, Charles at BRIDGE OF ALLAN, by D. Angus. pph. 60p (p&p 50).

10 DOUNE, by Moray Mackay – historical notes. 126pp. 1955, publ. 1984. £3.50 (p&p £1.20). (0.9506962.5.0)

11 DOUNE – postcards from the past, by McKenzie. 40pp. 1988. (p&p 60).

12P EARLY GRAVESTONES IN HOLY RUDE CHURCHYARD. J. Harrison. pph £1.50 (p&p 50).

13 THE FORTH NATURALIST & HISTORIAN – annual – from 1976, is supported by BP. Each volume of c130pp. has climate and bird reports for central Scotland, 6 to 8 naturalist and historical articles, book reviews and notes. Preprints may be available c 5p per page, some are available as pamphlets.

Vol 16 Nov. '93, University Jubilee Issue, £4, incl. Recent changes, weather C Scotland; Birds – a conservationist's view; Bird communities, Oak and Norway Spruce Loch Lomondside; Lime supply 14th-18thC; Sport and recreation; Bridge of Allan, Queen of Scottish Spas; The University – 25 years impact on Stirling; Voters of Clackmannan in 1832; Last execution in Stirling; Alan Mair. (SBN 1-898008-01-9. Back vols at reduced prices (each) – Vols 2,3,4,6 at 50p; 1 and 5 £1; 7-10 £1; 11 £2; 12 £1.50; 13 £2; 14 £4; 15 £3.50 (p&p 70). Three 5yr List/Indexes 1-, 6-, 11-, 40p; some papers are available as separates or pamphlets from Editor, e.g. Airthrey Roads; Ashfield Factory Village; Climate, Bird and Flora papers. Papers/notes for publication are welcomed.

Vol 17 (1.898008.02.7) Nov. '94. £5, includes Bridge of Allan's Musical Heritage; New light on RLS; Community Woodlands; Mountain Hare in the Ochils; Launching Forth, neglected river; Blairlogie; Mineral resource recovery – Silver Mine; Ancient Bridge of Stirling; David Bruce – People of the Forth (3) part 2 – short notes on a rare grass and a dragonfly; Book notes/reviews.

14 THE LURE OF LOCH LOMOND by R M McAllister. c50pp in preparation. (0.9514147.6.3).

15 MINES AND MINERALS OF THE OCHILS. CFSS. 44pp. 1994. Reprint. £1.50 (p&p 60).

16 THE OCHIL HILLS – Landscape, Wildlife, Heritage, Walks, by L Corbett et al. 60pp. May '94. (0.9506962.3.4) £3.50 (p&p 70).

17P THE SCOTTISH ENCLOSURES – 18C farming and landscape, by L Stewart. pph £1 (p&p 60).

18P SMITH, T S – artist, founder of Stirling's Art Gallery and Museum, by Jamieson and Paton. pph £1 (p&p 60).

19P ST MARGARET, QUEEN OF SCOTLAND, by S M Macpherson. pph 60p (p&p 40).

20P (STEVENSON) R L S AT BRIDGE OF ALLAN, by D Angus. £1. (p&p 50).

21P STEVENSON and the TROSSACHS, by L Stott. pph 80p (p&p 40).

22P STIRLING JOURNAL INDEX, 1820-1970, 3 vols. Vol 1 (1820-60) is out of print, reduced £2 each (p&p £2.50 if not collectable).

MAPS – LOCAL AREAS

23 GODFREY 15"/m reprints of 25"/m 1890s OS maps, folded (some available flat) at £1.85 each (p&p 50) 25 titles commissioned by FN&H – Alloa; Alva/Tullibody/Menstrie; Balfron/Killearn; Bannockburn; Bathgate; Bo'ness; Bridge of Allan; Doune/Callander; Clackmannan and Kincardine; Denny; Dollar/Muckhart; Dunblane East & West; Dunipace; Falkirk; Grangemouth; Larbert/Stenhousemuir; Linlithgow; Polmont; Stirling – 4 maps – St Ninians; Stirling North; Stirling 1896; Stirling and District; Tillicoultry. NB All have historical notes or in adjoining maps e.g. for Denny see Dunipace; for Dunblane West see Dunblane East; for the four Stirling maps see Stirling 1896 and Stirling and District. Also available – Perth, Dundee, Kilmarnock, Edinburgh, Glasgow, and others in Scotland.

Some titles are out of print, e.g. Clackmannanshire – historical sources; Making of Modern Stirling; Woollen Mill Buildings.

Discount terms to trade, and societies, delivery charged for small orders. Pay on order or within 30 days, 90 at less discount, 'Forth Naturalist and Historian'. Cheques or BACS Bank of Scotland 80-91-29 Acc 00251348.

(LC Nov. 1995)